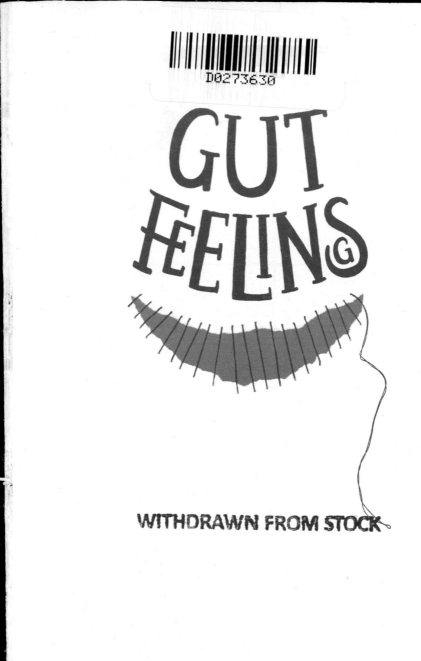

GUT FEELINS

C. G. MOORE

GUT FEELINGS

uclanpublishing

Gut Feelings is a uclanpublishing book

First published in Great Britain in 2021 by
uclanpublishing
University of Central Lancashire
Preston, PR1 2HE, UK

978-1-9129-7943-1

1 3 5 7 9 10 8 6 4 2

Text design by Becky Chilcott.

A CIP catalogue record for this book is available from the British Library.

Printed and bound in Great Britain by Clays Ltd, Elcograf S.p.A.

Light stronger than the Sun,
More pearlescent than the Moon,
More beautiful than a shooting star.

To Mam,
Words will never be able to capture
what you mean to me.

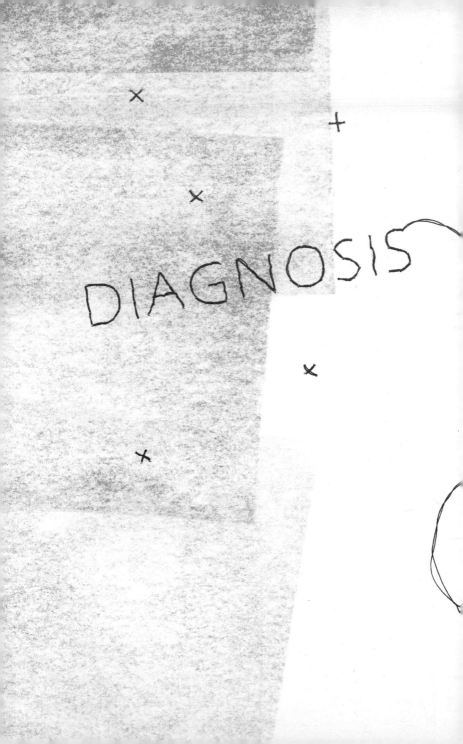

DIAGNOSIS

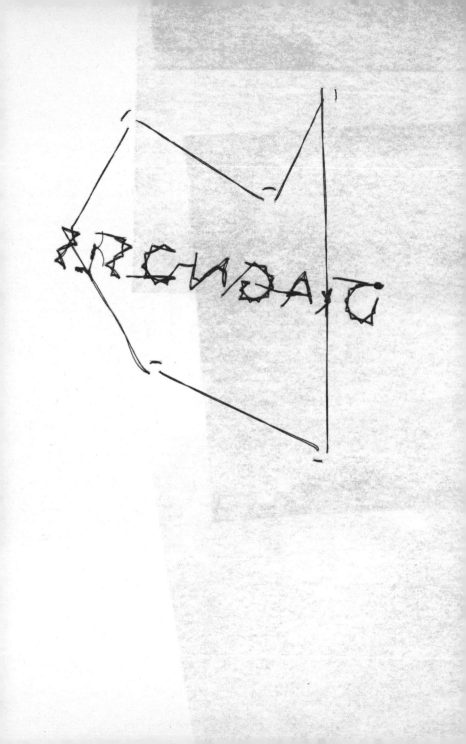

ELEVEN-NESS

Eleven should be care-free youth
Bubbling in veins,
Pitching balls into baskets
And crafting muskets
From tinfoil and
Imagination.

Eleven should be about
Making memories
Wishing wishes and
Living life without a care;
Playing, laughing, smiling, thinking,
Jumping, running, cycling, singing.

Eleven should be everything
And anything
It's wanted to be,

    But for me
        It's different;
            A spectre,
                An itch

Burrowing deep under my skin;
A dark mark staining my blood,
Branding my heart.
Even though it hasn't been confirmed,
I feel it swirling beneath my skin.

POLY – WHAT?

I sit and pray and wait and try
To tell myself little truths,
Little lies.
Polyposis:
It doesn't sound like cancer,
Like tiny wart like lumps —
Little time bombs waiting to explode

And spread the C-word through my system.

I
Do
Not
Understand
Any
Of
This.

BLOOD TEST

Blood flows through the tube;
Funny how it can tell so much,
Know so much of who we are,
Hold secrets that our brains cannot fathom.

My blood will be sent off.
We will see if I have the gene.
All that runs through my mind is
Cancer. Cancer. Cancer. Cancer.

CANCER

A star sign —
The crab.
A constellation —
Fault in Our Stars.
A film —
American documentary.
A song —
Sung by *My Chemical Romance.*
Tropic —
Circle of latitude.
Music —
A British death metal band.
Cancer —
Death's kiss.

DIAGNOSIS

Dad pats me roughly on the back
As if this will scrape up the sands of time
With bitten, bloodied nails,
Erasing the bad news from
memory,

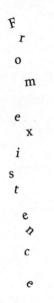

His lips move
But I cannot hear;
I taste salt on my tongue,
Feel tears flow in tributaries
That hands fail to wipe away.

SUNDAYS

Every Sunday
Dad takes me to the park
To watch the boys
Play football.

My eyes follow the boys —
Not the ball
As it pinballs

Up

and

down

The pitch.

The whistle blows;
I chase dad,
Taking the five euro note
That flutters
Into my hands.

In clouds of cigarette smoke
And boyish bravado,
I laugh
With the boys,
Never once looking
At the girls.

Time flies by and
Dad places a firm hand
On my shoulder,
Holding onto me
As he wobbles home.

Have fun? he asks.
I nod,
Holding my nose
Against b e e r
              b r e a t h.

TOGETHER WE CRY

Dad drives the car,
His eyes welling as he turns
Into unfamiliar territory.

Beside me, mam pats my back,
Like this will take away the darkness
Growing inside me.

Emotion silences us.
Futures frighten us.
Silence smothers us.

MONEY MEANS NOTHING

I take the €100 note
From dad's callused hands,
Thanking him with a forced smile.
Money cannot buy us minutes
Though we spend hours
Chasing coins,
While bleeding limited life
Spent with family.

GRANDAD

Grandad died
Seven years ago.
It doesn't stop my mind
Conjuring memories:

Dancing in springtime cherry blossoms,
Ice cream by the beach in summer,
Crunching autumnal leaves,
Wrapped up warm in winter.

He had FAP,
Just like mam,
Just like me —
I struggle onwards
Without him.

I miss him
More than words
Can ever say.

FAP IS . . .

fa*mil*ial / ad*e*no*mat*us / pol*yp*o*sis

Definition of familial adenomatous polyposis:

A rare condition
Affecting colon and rectum.
Cause: a faulty gene.
An invisible illness,
Inherited condition,
Chronic disease –
A silent killer
If left untreated.

DR BOURKE

Dr Bourke is
An ordinary man
Just like any other;
Greying hair,
Stubbled,
Weathered hands
Wielding scalpels.

Not one of
The handsome doctors
From the TV.

I watch his lips move,
Mam nods.

Have you any questions?

All I have are questions:
Why me?
What does this mean?
When will I be better?

Dr Bourke speaks
In medical terms
My twelve-year-old brain
Cannot comprehend.

FIRST DAY

I enter the classroom,
Take a seat
In the middle;
Far away
To avoid questions,
Far away
From teachers' gazes.

Boys
I do not know
Kick the legs
Of my chair.

What is it they want
This time?

The bell rings.
I push back
From the desk
In time to hear
Them hiss:
Gay
Bender
Faggot.

SCIENCE

How we are,
Why we are,
How we work
Fascinates me;
Demands my attention
In a way
Nothing else can.

From Darwin to Newton,
I thirst to know more:
About who we are —

Who
I
Am,
How
I
Should
Be.

POETRY

Poetry alludes me,
Hidden codes
I cannot crack.

Words whirl around me,

Refusing to stay still

Long enough for me

To feel their force.

a

E

W

H

L

J

c

k

n

U

i

B

v

t

s

f

g

p

X

d

r

D

y

SHADOW

First years circle,
Swarming in large groups;
Laughing,
Whispering,
Shouting —
All the while,
I wait on the fringes,
Silent prey;
Determined to avoid capture.

O

Q

m

C

h

R

i

s

Z

MY FIRST COLONOSCOPY

A letter arrives in the post
Marking my colonoscopy date.
I do not understand
Any of this.

Mam says,
It's a camera up your bum.
Is this is supposed to make me feel better?
It makes me feel like vomiting up a kidney.

I Google torture devices,
Wondering how they'll squeeze
A camera up there.

I shut my laptop,
Curl into a ball,
Hold knees to chest.

It's like swimming
In an ocean of sharks,
Never knowing:
Will I be bitten?

COUNTDOWN

I sit alone
In the dark,
Punching buttons
On a controller,
Watching as pixelated bullets
Zoom across the screen.

Mam tells me:
You need fresh air,
Go out with your friends.

How do I say
My friends have abandoned me?

66 BOXES

☒ I cross out another box,

☐ Another day

☐ Closer to my surgery.

☐ Worry claws my insides

☐ As my mind flits between

☐ Scalpels,

☐ Medication,

☐ Isolation.

☐ 66 more boxes to tick:

☐ Freedom descends

☐ With the Sun.

THWACK

I kick the ball
Against the fence.

Thwack.

I imagine boys my age
Kicking the ball
To me.

Thwack.

Jason, Liam,
Martin, Nick.

Thwack.

I wish I had
Someone to talk to
Now.

Thwack.

The balls flies
Into the air,
Whooshing past me.

FASTING

Crackers inches from my lips —
Mam reminds me
It's after midnight,
I'm fasting.

I tilt my plate,
Up high.
My midnight snack
Slides into the bin.

Stomach grumbling,
I stomp
Up the stairs and
Into bed.

BLIND OBEDIENCE

Nurse: Put this on.
I obey.
Nurse: Take off your shoes.
I obey.
Nurse: Sit on the bed.
I obey.

This room is no place
For a child
That wants to run and swim,
Bike his way
To the top of the hill.
I listen and obey
As curtains close
Around me —
Around my future.

MIND RACING

The blue dressing grown
Scratches my skin.

I stare at the white walls,
Waiting:

For the procedure.
For the surgery.
For my life
To trundle its way
Back on track.

ENEMA

Knees to your chest,
The nurse tells me.
I catch a glimpse of the enema;
I feel sick.
A hand on my cheek.
Relax.
It is like telling
A skydiver to relax before he

J
U
M
P
S

Out of the plane.
Deep breath in –
It sounds like an order.

I want it to stop.
I can't find my voice.
It hurts.

The nurse says,
Just like jelly
As the enema is
Pushed inside me,
Liquid filling my rectum.

Jelly is harmless though;
It's not supposed to go
Inside your bum.

My eyes well.
I can't help it.

Hold it in as
L   O   N   G
As you can.
Foetal position:
I can't relax.
Just like jelly.

Just.

Like.

Jelly.

WARRIOR

Mam makes silly faces,
Sticks out her tongue,
Tells me stories
I've heard
A thousand times.
It soothes my pain.
I smile through discomfort:
I have a warrior
Fighting my corner.

FLUSH

I lock the door,
Undo the ties on my gown,
Squat on the seat.
Disinfectant overpowers the smell
Of poo.

I need to go —
I hesitate.
My bowel makes the decision
For me.
Liquid fire
Burns my cheeks,
Splattering the basin.

The room spins.
I feel sick.
I clean myself

F L U S H

I walk to the door but
Collapse in a heap,
Counting down the minutes
Until my world stops spinning —
It never does.

COLONOSCOPY

The anaesthetist injects something clear
Into my veins.
I feel fuzzy within minutes.

Dr Bourke talks to me, asking,
How old are you?
How is school?
Are you going on holiday?
Questions that mean little and
Do nothing to quell my terror.

I want to cry but
My tear ducts are frozen shut.

I want to scream but I have no voice.
My body fails to respond –
No one can see my pain.

They roll me onto my side and
Someone shoves a tube between my cheeks

I don't fe

WHERE AM I?

My vision is blurry.
I blink but
It does not clear.

He's awake, a woman says,
But I cannot turn my head.

My body is not my own;
Numbed by chemicals.

I'm burning,
Sweat blanketing my skin.

My stomach heaves.
I'm gonna —

I vomit everywhere.
Someone tilts my head.

Where am I?
You're safe, the woman soothes,

Only . . .

GOOD JOB

Good job, Dr Bourke tells me.
I pray for good news but
This is me and
I've come to expect the worst.

He talks in medical terms:

APC gene:
A major gene
Involved in causing colorectal cancer.

Polyps:
Small growths,
Usually benign,
With a stalk protruding
From a mucous membrane.

Dysplasia:
Presence of cells
Of an abnormal type
Within a tissue –
May signify a stage
Preceding the development
Of cancer.

I don't understand but
His conclusion bleeds into my ears:
Surgery.
Soon.

21.

Have
This
Surgery.

He won't see 21
If he doesn't.

WHAT THIS MEANS

Surgery
Meds
Preventative
More surgery
Stronger meds
Pre-emptive
More surgery
More frequent meds
Protective
More surgery
Proactive
To try to carve this spectre
From my bowel.

WISHES

Polyps crowd the walls of my bowel
Like galaxies of stars
Lighting up the midnight sky.
Clear, cloudless, still —
They can be seen a world away.

I sit and stare
At the picture
Of my colon.
My stomach is lead.
My legs are jelly.
My eyes see everything
But take in nothing.

Vomit rises in my throat —
Still I stare.
There's something strange and spellbinding
About seeing microscopic carcinogens
Coating my insides
Like a river of blisters,
Pouring into a sea of pink and yellow.

POLYPS

Small growths with
Stalks protruding from
Mucous membranes.

Little lumps
Lining the walls
Of my bowel.

Wart-shaped,
Ready to infect,
To spread.

Tiny in size,
Deadly in nature —
My malignant polyps.

Abnormal:
Capable of
Taking life.

THE PHONE CALL

In McDonalds,
We talk animatedly.
Until mam gets a
Phone call.

She answers, smiling,
But the smile disappears.
Mam moves away,
Out of earshot.

My sister and aunt
Jabber on.
All of this feels like a
Performance.

Mam whispers to my aunt.
Aunty Anna's smile is now
An upside-down frown.
Mam leaves.

You'll love the pantomime, Anna tells me.
I'm so confused.
I hate pantomimes
And I don't know what's happened

To mam.

THE PANTOMIME

Oh no it isn't,
Oh yes, it is.

Voices swell around me
But I feel alone.

Oh no you don't,
Oh yes, I do.

The smell of buttered popcorn
Fills up the auditorium.

Oh no it doesn't,
Oh yes, it does.

Anna bites her nails,
Jaw clenched, watching the show.

Oh no it isn't,
Oh yes, it is.

Screams fill the auditorium,
My silent scream lost among them.

HE'S JUST SLEEPING

He's just sleeping, they tell me,
But I can see.
My father.

Crisp, white, linen sheets
Next to wooden seats.
Our agony.

The smell of disinfectant lingers
Like Death's chilled, clawing fingers.
Our fear.

Beep-beep-beep, sounds his lifeline,
Reminding us of hourglass time.
Our nemesis.

So fragile sleeping in his bed,
Throats clogged with hope and dread.
My observation.

Family feed me lie after lie,
To protect me, they will deny
Me the truth I so desperately crave;
That there's zero chance for him to be saved.

My father:
Farther from me than ever before
While a broken family
Waits by the door.

THE WAITING ROOM

In the waiting room,
My mother's friends and
My father's family
Lock horns.
Family who are distant and cold
Crawl out of their caves
To visit their dying sibling
Lest they look bad.
My mother's friends,
Warm and full of life,
Created memories with my father
On an almost-daily basis.
My grandmother cannot understand
Why she is not his next-of-kin.
My mother enters the room,
A broken woman,
As vitriol flows
From his family's mouths.

A MEMORY

My father works high
Atop a hill
In a touch-the-sky
Stone building.
He holds the door open,
Introducing me to his co-worker
Who gushes at how cute I am.
I'm not cute:
I am 7.
She gives me a euro before
Dad leads me out.
I see him key in a code
Giddy with the knowledge,
He leads me to the empty cells,
The kitchen and,
Finally,
The games room.
We play pool
Until my hands cramp.
Dad walks me down the hill
Where we sit on the sea wall,
Watching the powerful waves
Wash against the sand banks,
Eating chips and battered sausages,
Drowning in curry sauce.

PRISONER

A prisoner to memories,
I stare at tight tubes
Snaking around dad's body,
Choking every inch
Of life
From his veins.

I remind myself
The nurses are helping,
The doctors performing
Last-minute miracles
To save
Our Father.

We whisper prayers
Between cracked lips,
From dry throats,
With watering eyes
As we plead for
Divine intervention.

GOOD IN GOODBYE

There's good in goodbye;
In telling friends
See you tomorrow,
In hugging family tight
At Christmas,
In moving on,
Moving up,
In sport,
In education,
In life,
But this kind of goodbye feels
Permanent.
Will the next time
I see my father
Be when we bury him?
I struggle to breathe,
To think.
Memories shatter my mind
Like rapid-firing machine guns.
Saying goodbye to my father is
Not telling him
I'll see you at home.
It's fearing
We'll see him at his funeral.

PADRE PIO'S GLOVE

A glove will never work:
It's a myth.
Don't delude yourself,
Religious nut, they told my mother
So
Why
Are
My
Father's
Eyes
Open?

THE CIRCUS

They take the tube
Out of his throat.
His voice is hoarse.
He doesn't say much.

Where are you?
The doctor asks.
The circus.
We laugh
But he's serious.
Outside his door
We cry.

A.B.I. IS

A girl's name –
Short for Abigail.
Association of British Insurers.
A village in Iran.
Applied Biosystems.

Acquired Brain Injury –
Caused by many things
But for my father,
A blood vessel burst on his brain.

Memories lost;
His temper will fray.
Be patient.
He won't play football again.
He can't hear too good.
He's still your dad
With short-term memory,
A short-term fuse but
A long-term stay at
The National Rehabilitation Centre.

ME AND MY DAD

Me and my miracle dad were
Never close.
When I was younger,
I
Played football,
Practised karate
To impress him.

I felt a failure
To the father I wanted to please.
At school,
I learned that words,
More than weapons,
Could destroy a body,
Tear out a heart,
Just as easily as a karate chop.

My dad was prickly
Like a hedgehog –
Hard to please and, once pleased,
Difficult to keep pleased.
He loved football and drinking
At the expense of family.

My father provided financially
But money does not equal love.

Love is born out of bedtime stories,
Kisses on cheeks,
From head to toe:
It consumes you.

Love was never his strong suit but
Watching my dad learn to eat again
Brings tears to my eyes and
A pain between my ribs that
No pill can
Heal.

I CAN NEVER FORGET

I can never forget
Weekends spent
In a smoky pub
Where my imagination took over
To cocoon me from horrors
I never should have seen.

I can never re-work the square
That was my father's love
When I was so clearly a circle.
I learned to fight with words;
I hid in books, living a thousand lives,
While my dad drunk his way through
His.

But
He's my family.
Watching him learn to walk
Tears me up inside.
I will never forget the past but
I cannot cling to it.
He is my father.
We might yet have
A future.

THE FIRST TIME

The first time
She left was
Heart-breaking.

Aunt Lena set
A plate of biscuits and
A cup of tea on the table while
Mam slipped
Out of the house.

I realised too late,
Footsteps retreating across concrete,
Racing towards Bayside.

Mam stood,
Waiting on the platform.
The green train whooshed by,
Swallowing her whole,
Whisking her away
While I watched
With watery eyes.

EMPTY

The empty chair

Between my sister and I

Pulls us in

like a black hole,

Ingesting
Emotion
Thought
Conversation
Until all we feel
At the dinner table is
Loss.

DRIVE

Today,
We drive to the
Rehab Centre
With mam.

I lower the window,
A breeze blasting my face
As I lean
Out of the car.

The seaweed scent is sharp —
It stings the senses
As we pass Booterstown,
Conjuring memories
Of Howth.

NATIONAL REHABILITATION CENTRE

Off-white walls:
This could be a
Civic centre,
Apartments
Or offices.

This a place for
People that are broken:
Limbs,
Hearts,
Minds.
It reminds me of hospital.
I swallow against
The sour taste of dread;
Enemas,
Surgery,
Medication,
Racing through my mind.
I shut the car door
As my sister and I
Accompany mam
To our father's bed.

WHEN ARE WE GOING HOME?

We pass through
Automatic doors,
Following mam as she weaves
Through corridors,
Signing the visitor book
As we enter dad's ward.

Dad looks glazed
When we arrive
By his bedside.

Mam fluffs his pillows,
Aids his short-term memory,
Feeds him tinned peaches
On a plastic spoon.

When are we going home?
It breaks my heart
To hear dad
Ask this.

He only just arrived.
What must it feel
To a man
Unsure if his memories are
Real?

LONGING

Uncle Gary takes us to the cinema,
Buys us buttery popcorn that
Transports me to the moment
Our lives changed.

Aunty Anna hosts a sleepover,
Letting us eat Chinese takeaway
In front of the TV,
Feet resting against soft carpet.

Aunt Lena offers us sweet treats
To take the edge off our pain,
Hot cups of tea
To warm my heavy heart.

None of this can change what's done.
My sister plays in the fields
With our cousins
While I stare out the window,
Legs curled under me,
Longing for mam's return.

MAKESHIFT MEALS

Thrown together dinners,
Overcooked but fallen upon,
Still better than lumpy mash,
Cold potato wedges and
Tough chicken
Served out of hatches
In the hospital canteen.
Pizza boxes
Spill from the green bin.
Health is not the focus
Of makeshift meals
Intended to satisfy
Immortal hunger.

RELATIVE ROULETTE

My sister and I
Play relative roulette
While my father learns to
Talk
Walk
Eat
Drink.

Aunt to uncle,
Uncle to aunt,
I wait for the careful

Tap

Tap

Tap

Of mam's approach,
     Of a fragmented family

    Stitching itself
       Back together.

WORRIES

Worries gnaw at my insides.

Worries for my father,
Who may never
Reclaim his past.

Worries for my mother,
Who drives a thousand miles
To endure a thousand screams.

Worries for my sister,
Who plays relative roulette:
Where will she stay tonight?

I worry, too, for me.
Struggling to see
My tomorrows:
Will these be my best days?
Worries gnaw me inside.

FEAR

Fear paralyses me,
Straitjackets my feelings,
Heightens my panic
As I struggle to breathe.
Always there,
At the back of my mind,
A sleeping beast,
Ready to stir.
Fear lives in the shadow
Of hope:
Slicing my insides,
Severing emotion,
Stifling thought.

NO ESCAPE

There's

No escape from the
Thundering

Of my heart
In my chest;
Of sweat on my tongue and
Tears in my eyes;
Of the sleeping god's hold
Over my once-pleasant dreams.

No escape from family that mean well,
Pats on the back and
Thoughtfully thoughtless sentiments
Reaching my ears.
No escape from mam's guilt
And dad's helplessness
As he lies bed-bound
Twenty miles away.

No escape from the clock
Counting down
Seconds
Minutes
Hours
Until the day
My life will
Change.

THE WAIT IS OVER

I see the hospital's stamp at the top,
My name in the middle,
Rattling the foundations
Of my fragile world.

I suck air through my lips,
Hiss it out again.
I tear at the envelope,
Extracting it
With stiff fingers.

Reading the letter,
I'm overcome;
Fear claws up my windpipe,
Eclipsing hope
From my mind.

The wait is over.

I hold fate in my hands.
The last grains of hourglass time
Slip through my fingers.
Seven days until my life is
Turned upside down
Once again.

TOTAL

Total colectomy:
The official name
For the procedure
I will have but
All I see is total,
Final,
Irreversible.

Total colectomy:
The removal of
My large intestine
To prevent
The growth of polyps.

Printed on the letter:
Total
Burns into my mind,
Makes my hands shake,
Replays my worst fears
On loop
TOTAL.

CRUMLIN CHILDREN'S HOSPITAL

It could be a funeral home,
This hospital,
From the outside –
All drab colours and no imagination.
We pass through automatic doors,
Greeted by cartoon knock-offs
Stencilled across damaged,
Death-infused walls.
Dog-eared games and dishevelled toys
Piled up high in a cardboard box.

Despite children and parents
Playing pat-a-cake,
The signs of lingering death
Overwhelm my senses.
A stale scent
Hangs in the air.
Suffocating, smoggy . . .

Children stir in shared rooms,
Wired to tubes
Inserted into wrists, arms and noses.
Hospital monitors
Beep-beep-beep while
Nurses and doctors
Thunder through white corridors.

The rainbow facade does
No more to comfort me than:

The grey brick
Boxing me into this prison

The invasive disinfectant smell

Trolleys being wheeled to theatre

Small, lifeless forms
Hooked up to beeping machines

You can paint these walls
In rainbow colours bright and bold,
Plaster the walls
With princes and princesses
But we all know
There is no gold
Waiting at the end.

SEALING MY FATE

The nurse is pleasant,
Asking questions about school while
She checks my blood pressure and
Pokes around in my ear
For a temperature reading.
Her name badge is framed
By two yellow, smiley faces.
She steps back,
Takes a laminated bracelet,
Pulling back the adhesive strip.
I hold out my wrist.
She clamps the name tag
Around my arm,
Sealing my fate.
The paper band feels like steel
Weighing down my hands.

GAMBLE

The view
From my room is
Of Star Bingo's,
Gaudy poster
Advertising cheap-as-chips games.

My life has been
One big game —
A gamble.
9,999 chances that
It wouldn't be me
Yet here I sit,
On a stiff bed,
Taking in a view
That would make Vegas jealous.

Cards on the table,
FAP raises the stakes:
I hold my breath,
Checking my hand,
Unsure if I can win
This game of life.

OOPSY DAISY

A jolly nurse
Bustles into the room
Wheeling a trolley
Of test tubes and needles.
Her enthusiasm,
More than her inability to hit a vein,
Makes me nauseous as
She takes three attempts
To extract a blood sample
From my bruised and battered arm.
Oopsy daisy,
She sing-songs,
Missing the vein yet again.
I gawk at my arm –
If she misses one more time,
I can join the dots
Into a diamond.

• 2

• 3

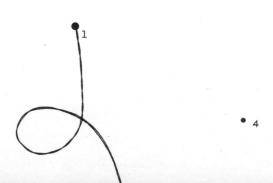

• 4

WANT A CHIP?

The baby next to me needs
A kidney transplant.
His days on borrowed time
Draw to an end and yet,
His family cuddle around him,
Smiles brightening lined faces with
Clouds of salt-and-vinegar heat
Steaming the window.
Dialysis is a cruel fate
For a child
Young enough to scream,
Not old enough to talk.

Want a chip?
The mother asks.
I shake my head.

I don't want any food
In my system
When I get the enema.
I take a minute,
Feeling Superman strength
Harden my bones.
Some people have it worse —
I *can* do this.

PICOLAX

What I fear most is the enema.
The nurse's voice still haunts my dreams:
Just like jelly.
I feel sick.

Mam explains about the enema and
They offer an alternative:
Picolax.
Laxatives.

I down five litres
Of blackcurrant Ribena
Mixed with citrusy Picolax powder.
I force it down,
Gagging,
Fighting back the urge to vomit.

Three hours pass.
I have not been to the toilet:
The nurses are not happy.

FEEL

Mam and I
Play cards,
Watch daytime TV,
Listen to the same
Song on repeat
Until I feel like
Unplugging the radio and
Chucking it from
This third-storey window.
A chipper woman opens the door,
Announcing that lunch is served.
Mam tells her I'm fasting.
I'm faint,
The white walls shake and blur
At the edges of my vision
I clench my fists,
Holding tight to that feeling.
I want to feel something when
They come for me.

JUST LIKE JELLY

Mam squeezes my hand tight.
Knees up past your belly.
Just like jelly.
I'm going to be sick.
It doesn't feel like jelly.
It hurts but
The nurse is doing a job;
She doesn't care,
Does nothing to comfort me
As my muscles protest
Against the nozzle
Of the enema.
Hold it in as
Long as you can.
Knees to my chest,
I wait.

FAR FROM OVER

We play I-Spy,
My cheeks burning
From repeated, return
Toilet trips.
TREE, mam yells as
The nurse appears.
Sympathy stains her face —
I already know what this is.
I clasp mam's hand tight.
She tells me stories
I've heard a hundred times as
The nurse inserts the enema,
Penetrating stubborn muscle while
Tears fall.
All done.
None of this *is* done though.
This isn't over.
This isn't my last enema,
My last surgery.
Fear grips my mind,
Tendrils hooking deep,
Tearing through
Flesh and bone.
This isn't over.

SHOOTING STAR

Mam holds my hand
Through the good,
The bad,
Easing the discomfort,
Shifting my focus
From enemas and fasting
To laughter and smiles.

Her hand is warm,
Gently caressing my skin,
Soothing my anxieties,
Quietening my nerves,
Conquering my inner demons that
Play distorted versions
Of the future
On loop.

My mother:
Light stronger than the Sun,
More pearlescent than the Moon,
More beautiful than a shooting star.

DON'T FEED THEM YOUR FEARS

Mam kisses me goodnight at 7pm
So she can visit dad.
Aunty Anna stays with me,
Making me laugh
Even though my cheeks burn and
The bedsores will make sleep
Impossible.

The nurse knock, knock, knocks –
An enema in her cardboard bowl.
I start but
The window is bolted shut and
She blocks the only exit.

Knees to chest:
Don't cry.
Just like jelly:
Don't cry.
Big, brave boy:
Don't cry.
Don't cry.

Do

Cry

Not

Do

STAY WITH ME

Stay with me
When the light blinks out

Alone

Stay with me
In the middle of the night

Anxious

Stay with me
Through night-time tests

Alarmed

Stay with me,
In theatre

Aghast

Stay with me,
Through leakages at night

Ashamed

Stay with me:
I cannot do this

Alone.

SECRET CITY

The elevator pings and
  Doors open.

An aquarium filled with colourful fish;
    Orange and gold and yellow and brown,
    Swim in and out of the windows of
    An underground city
    With sleek, metallic walls and
    Monuments built to echo
    Dublin City.

  I close my eyes.
  I am a fish,
 Swimming
In and out
Of tiny holes,
  Powering through
   A world of dreams and imagination.
    I am free to flee from
      Stubby fingers that
        Smudge the walls of my world.

The goldfish world
Grows smaller,
   Disappearing from sight as
   I am wheeled
   Towards my fate.

WEEEEEEEEEEE!

It's funny how a single motion
Conjures a dozen memories.

Being wheeled to theatre
Reminds me of my terror,
Of losing control,
Being thrust into the air
Kicking my legs high
For the first time,
Of
Falling,
Falling,
Falling,
Towards concrete after
Rough hands pushed me
Down,
Down,
Down.

It reminds me of
Jumping in the air and
Screaming at the top of my lungs.

SOARING

The doctors have given
Something to relax me,
Something to take the edge
Off my fears.
My hands flop over the rails
Of my bed and
I kick off the scratchy blankets.
The orderlies try to restrain me but
I'm a bird
Soaring,
Soaring,
SOOOOOOAAARRRRRRRRRIIIIIIIIINNNNNGGGGGGGGG
So high that
I cackle all the way to theatre.

THE ANAESTHETIST

They look like aliens,
Mouths and bodies
Masked in blue-green scrubs.
Dr Bourke asks me
Question after question
Before telling me that
It's time to go to sleep.
The anaesthetist,
Myself reflected in his glasses,
Adjusts the mask
Over my mouth and nose.
I inhale gas that smells of
Sickness
Science
Surgery.
I ponder how long it will —

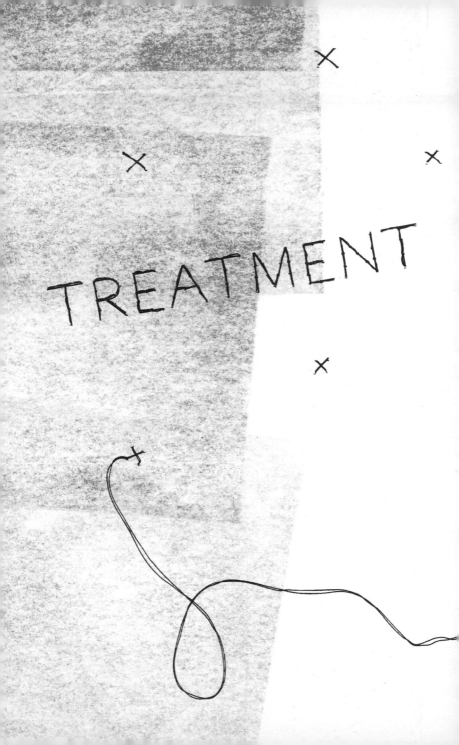

TREATMENT

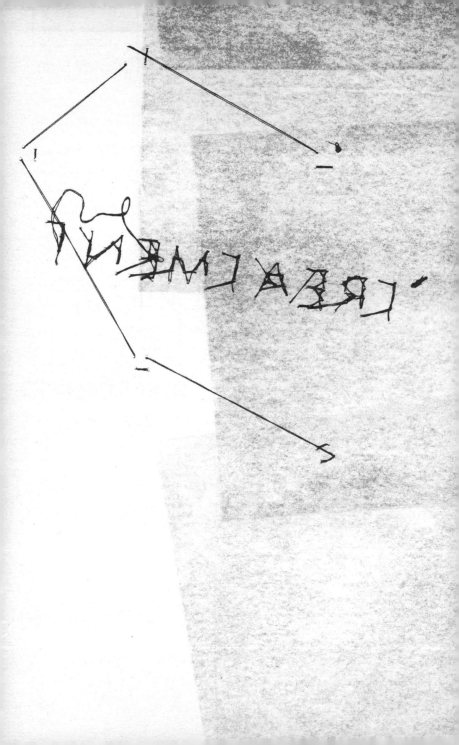

DRUGGED UP

You did it, I exclaim,
Jabbing my finger at the window.
Rain pelts down like bullets.
I cower under blankets,
Tossing,
Turning,
Kicking,
Curling into a tiny ball,
Shutting out the universe.

MORPHINE

morphine
unlike anything
i've experienced
flying
outside body
i see mam,
sitting on cotton cloud
words whirling
head fuzzy
dizzy
a maelstrom of
fears
failures
social pressures
sliding
on all sides

r

o

e
v
a
p

a t i

n

g

**feels good
liberating
my mind;
bathing in
freedom**

HOOKED UP

An IV drip snakes
Around my arm,
Draining life
From my veins.
I close my eyes,
Listening to disconcerting sounds
Of beeping machines,
Squeaking shoes and
Trolleys wheeling
Past my room.

I close my eyes,
Wishing this away,
Pretending the beeping is
The airplane noise
The captain makes
When the plane
Soars through the sky.

With my left hand —
My bad hand —
I feel a tube running
Into my boxers,
Another tube
Feeding my body and
A third in my nose.

I am constricted by tubes

Like a puppet

Hoisted up and

Marched around

On marionette strings.

TENDER

My searing scar
Screams
As the nurse
Changes the bandages.

When her fingers press,
Pain erupts
Through my body.

I suck a breath
Through my nose,
Exhale through my lips,
Counting the seconds
Until I hear her retreating steps.

WHAT TO EXPECT

They told me
What to expect
Before the surgery
But living it is
Different
To reading booklets and
Listening
To formulaic conversation.

Pain b u b b l e s

Beneath the scar.
The nurse injects something
Through my veins
Intended to help:
No water can pass
Through my cracked lips.

TEAM

A team
Accompanies Dr Bourke
When he pulls back the curtain.
Curious junior and senior doctors
Stare at the captive animal,
Caged in;
His case is
Rare.

He asks doctor questions:

How are you feeling?
Hungry
Tired
Sore.

Does this hurt?
You poked my scar:
What do you think?

Would you like anything?
My life back.

They depart,
Pulling the curtains
Back into place.

FIRST STEPS

My body is stiff,
Sore with the effort
Of not disturbing
Winding tubes.
Today,
I take my first steps
Post-surgery.

PLAYROOM

The nurses tell mam
About a pantomime viewing
In the playroom.
Mam encourages me to go.
I wonder if this reminds her of dad too.
Lying in a hospital bed,
Alone.

With an entourage of family,
I wheel my IV drip
Down the corridor.
We open the door
To a zoo of boisterous
Girls and boys.

I take a seat near the back,
Forcing a smile.
I wonder if my cousins detest
Pantomimes as much as I do.
Everyone screams *oh no you didn't*,
Echoing around my memories.

LET'S PLAY PRETEND

My cousins say
How exciting the show was.
I want to scream.
I'm not stupid;
They enjoyed the show
As much as I'd enjoy
Eating battery acid.
I close my eyes because
When they leave,
I can cry myself to sleep.

MS RYAN

Ms Ryan coughs daintily
As she enters the room.
She smiles sadly,
Taking in the sight
Of one of her history students
Lying hooked up to machines.

She offers me chocolates
I cannot eat and
Fizzy drinks
I cannot drink.

I thank her,
Tell her I feel great,
Ask how she is.

Before she leaves,
She hands me a card
With messages
From the boys in my class.

School unnerves me —
I have no friends —
But it makes me smile
To know that
Someone is thinking

Of me.

COFFIN LIFE

I lie corpse-still,
Awaiting a miracle.
Hooked to machines,
Enshrouded in tangled tubes,
Kept alive by liquid sustenance
For 72 hours —
I have learned not to move.
I turn my head to the right,
Staring out at magpies
Soaring from branch to branch.
Turning to the left,
I hear the wet squeaks
Of shoes on lino:
The sounds of freedom,
So close but
So far away.
I'd cross my arms
Over my chest but
Triggering the machines will
Signal the nurses.
Instead,
I embrace my coffin life,
Staring at re-runs on TV
Over and over
Again.

YOU'RE SO BIG

You're so big,
Mam says,
Which feels a stupid thing to tell
Someone who is tied up with tubes —
Denied food and water

I was so skinny when I had my op.
I forgot skinny is synonymous with chic.
What a ridiculous thing to say and yet,
I tug at my flabby sides,
Wondering why I am so fat.

FAMILIAR FACES

Familiar faces,
Well-intentioned,
Peer through
The microscope,
Observing my pains
As I turn uncomfortably
In this blanketed tomb.
They offer gifts:
Food,
Drinks,
Plush toys,
To unknowingly
Tease and torment
Through a week
Without food,
Without water,
Without fresh
Lungfuls of air.
They tell me stories
I don't care about;
About people I don't know.
They offer sympathy
For something
They do not understand,
Could *never* understand —
Will *never* try to understand.

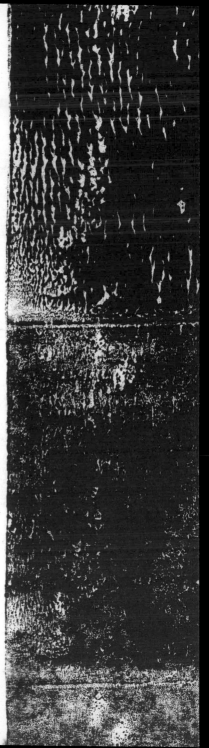

They have no idea what it's like
To be confined to this prison,
Bars lining the windows,
Double glazing boxing me in —
These familiar faces have
No idea how to reach me.

DAY 5

Five days without food is like never –

Seeing the sun rise,
Observing an eerie full Moon,
Feeling snow dust your face as
Winter winds whip against your cheeks.
Tasting lemon meringue pie;
The melt-in-your-mouth sweetness
Nestled on top of a bed
Of sharp, citrus curd and
A bed of crumbly, crunchy pastry.

Feeling the lips of a lover,
Locking hips
And staring into the eyes
Of someone who lies
Next to you at night,
Legs intertwined,
Bodies aligned,
In love.

It's like
Never living,
Never loving.
The pain in my stomach
Mirrors pains in my heart.

I want to
Tear at the tubes,
Race to the canteen and
Fight to the death
For a slice of stale bread.

GLOCKENSPIEL

I've lost two stone.
I
Guess
Six
Days
Without
Food
Will do that to a body.

The drip feeds my organs but
Dulls my mind.

Mam reads *OK! Magazine* while
I look at my belly.
I can count all
Twenty-four ribs
Protruding through opaque skin,
Demanding to be seen,
Monstrous and mesmerising.

I take mam's coffee stirrer
From my table.
She peers over her magazine as
I drum the stirrer across my ribs
Making sounds with my mouth
As I play my ribcage
Like a glockenspiel.

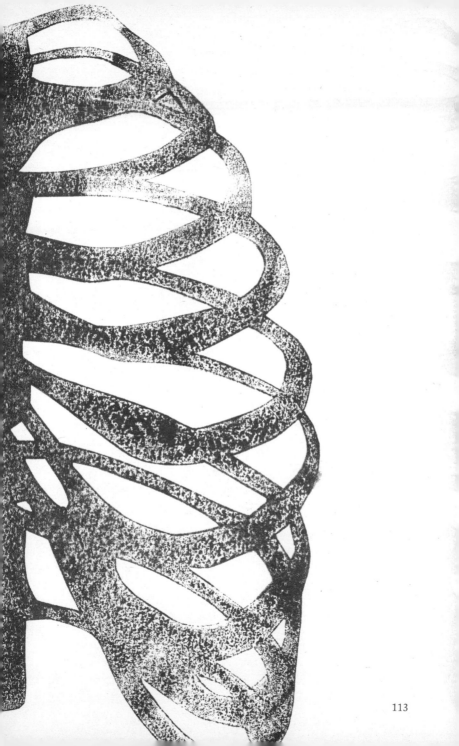

HELP

In the middle
Of the night,
I writhe as
Violent pain
Consumes every part of me.
Doubled over,
I reach for the call bell
And
F
A
I
L.

I scream.
Footsteps slap against cheap lino.
The door swings open.
Are you OK?
Hurt makes my world helter-skelter.
Cramps?
I shake my head.
Another pain takes over.

ADHESIONS

Adhesions,
They said.
I wondered how
Such a sonorous
Word could panic
And poison as much
As it has this last hour.
A whetted blade slicing me from the inside out.
Shredding.
Slicing.
Separating
Me
From

m

y

b

o

d

y

WATER

The nurse sets a cup of water
By my bedside.

I sip gently
As instructed.

Too much:
I might vomit.

Too little:
Thirst will not be quenched.

I run my tongue
Over cracked lips.

Cool and crisp:
I drink slowly.

PERFECT WHITE CIRCLES

The nurse enters my room
In the evening,
Introducing me to
A new medication.

Perfect, white circles:
Three to be taken
Eight times daily.
Twenty-four tablets:
I gawk.

The nurses tell me this is
Normal.
I'm not sure what normal is
Anymore.

They hand me three tablets.
I swallow them with a single mouthful
Of water.

Is this my life?
Tablets:
Different colours
Different shapes
That will make me appear
Normal?

LOMOTIL

I read the label carefully:
Lomotil.
lo
    mo
        til

 It sounds soft and safe,

Like a snail Inside its shell. I hold three pills In my palm, Placing them on my tongue, Swallowing.

ARE YOU STILL HERE?

Dr Bourke passes my door,
Peeps his head inside —
Eyebrows raised.

Are you still here?
I nod
Like it isn't obvious.

Have you eaten?
I shake my head.
I would kill for a single grape.

He frowns.
Let me see what I can do,
He disappears.

He returns.
All sorted,
He informs me, smiling.

I smile.
Dr Bourke is a lifeboat
In a sea of hunger.

Are you OK?
I nod.
Speaking takes up too much energy.

Take it easy, he replies,
Ignoring what is so clearly
A lie.

FIRST MEAL

After they discharge me.
Mam stops at McDonald's —
The first sign of hot food
On a long return home.
I order a double cheeseburger and
Medium fries.
In the car,
I bite into the burger,
Salivating as grease
Runs down my face.
I swallow fatty meat
With two, over-salted fries;
Chasing my hunger,
Famished to full up
In seconds.

REPEAT

53 months to acclimatise
To a life
Turned upside down.

1,610 days to re-train
My body
To eat, drink, sleep.

96,600 hours to live
A life
Changed by scalpels and scars.

5,796,000 minutes to forget
All that
I've lived through.

347,760,000 seconds until
I live it
All over again.

I can never forget.

WHERE ARE YOU NOW?

People crowded my hospital bed
All at once.

Now that I'm home,
Lying in my own bed,
The only visitors I receive are
Spectres that haunt
My dreams.
The surgery has fixed me —
I'm no longer worthy
Of attention and support.

My illness is a chronic one but
There is no one around me
To explain that to.
I turn over and close my eyes
Against the stadium-sized void
They've left behind.

FALLING APART

Mam sets my soup
Down by my bedside.
I've been home two days,
Refusing to leave my room.
She suggests we go for a walk.
Maybe:
A nice way of telling her
Never.
I'm not sure how she coped –
The cramps and adhesions,
The perfect white circles,
The scars marring body and mind.
This is one of three surgeries and
Already
I feel like falling apart.
I mute the TV and
Turn on my side.
I'm home now.
I'm safe.
So why does this bedroom
Feel like a prison?

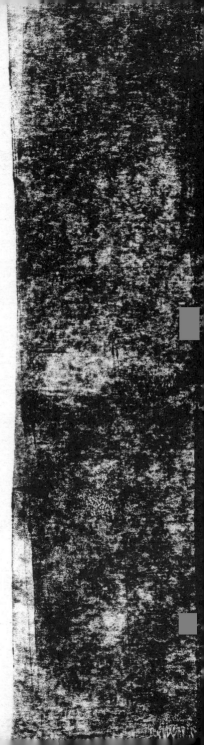

TIME

I should be skipping
Across the concrete,
Celebrating a successful surgery.
All I can think of is
The hourglass standing
Beside me;
Sand slipping through glass
Until I face my second surgery.
The not-knowing kills me.
Four years,
Of counting days
Until it starts over again.

BUBBLE BURST

13 years
Of swimming lengths,
Eating what I liked,
When I liked;
Of breaking the glass ceiling
And dreaming of the future.

132 months
Of dreaming hopeful things
That might one day come true;
Of winning galas
And celebrating with popcorn and lemonade.

4,018 days
Of beach days in Rush
And reading books in the sun;
Of rugby-tackling friends
In the golden sand,
Speeding towards the sea,
Cutting through the waves,
Stroke after glorious stroke.

13 should be anything
I want it to be
But now,
An eternity

Of careful eating,
Of smashed mirrors,
Of a t-shirt that will never come off
Except in the darkness of my room.

LIMITS

At school,
I must
Take meds
At precise times,
Avoid strenuous activities,
Choose from limited
Food options
To prevent cramps and
Diarrhoea.
My mind is flooded
With new information,
New ways
To control
My altered body.
But everyone has limits –
Things they cannot do.
I hold this thought close
As I march forward
Into the unknown.

RETURN TO SCHOOL

What happened?
Anthony asks.
I had a total colectomy.
He scratches his head.
I had my large intestine removed.
Why?
I was developing cancer.
The C-word usually shuts down discussion.
Anthony ponders this.
Did you lose weight?
Two stone.
So why doesn't everyone have it removed?
Good question, I reply,
Wondering how he made it
Into Honours Science.

PREY

Marcus K
Saw an easy target in me.
Hiding my schoolbag,
Dumping pencil parings into my hair,
Dead-arming me.
I wince when he appears.
I'm sorry about your father.
I didn't know.
Does it
Make him feel better
To say sorry for
Brutally beating kids
Quieter than him?
No problem.
I speed away,
Knowing that school is not forever.
I will be his prey once more
When dad is home.

LOCKER ROOM

I look at the boys
In my class
With adolescent curiosity,
Admiring beauty as
I try desperately
To deny that I'm different.

In the locker room,
I stick to dark corners,
Hiding my scar,
Concealing my shame.

Trapped by insecurity,
Jeers and jibes are
Aimed at me like missiles
Of fear and loathing.

Bet he likes seeing us in our boxers.

Stop looking at us!

Faggot.

Pinned down by shame,
I am not looking
At the boys in my class now.

Dead-arms and projectiles are
Sharp reminders that
Different is dangerous
At my school.

FAMILY WEEKEND

My scars are still tender but
It's mid-term break.
Mam's bringing dad home
From the Rehabilitation Centre
For the weekend.

He calls for our dog —
Lady.
When mam tells him
She's dead,
He sobs into his shirt sleeve.
My body has been altered;
I don't know if I could survive
If it was my mind.

Dad watches TV,
Zombified —
Cycling through channels
At a snail's pace.

It could be worse,
I tell myself,
Watching my father
Struggle to open a can of peaches.
I offer to help and
His shoulders deflate.

RETURN

Dad cries
As mam opens
The car door.

I stare out
From a crack
In my curtains.

Dad turns
From the passenger door,
Looking right at me:

His sight is poor —
Does he see me?
Does he ever really *see* me?

TEMPORARY HOME

Dad has returned
To his temporary room,
His temporary home.

For the next two months,
He will arrive back
On weekends,
Dizzy with excitement.

Returning on Mondays,
Crying and despondent,
As mam closes
The car door.

TUG O' WAR

Patients' families	Have been invited
To a BBQ,	To help loved ones
Feel more welcome,	More supported
More loved	While they fix
Broken bodies and minds	At the NRC.
I go to spend time	With mam —
I cannot be separated	From her
Any longer.	In this family tug-o'-war.

DESIRE

Mam introduces me
To the families;
Names I forget instantly,
Faces fading.
I take the food
I am given:
Sandwiches,
Sausages,
Salad,
Eating in silence,
Flashing a ceramic smile
To those that see me.
My sister bounds
Onto the bouncy castle.
I look on,
Wishing I could
Be that carefree.
Mam talks to a man
With brown stubble and
Kind blue eyes,
Metres from where I sit.
Palms sweating,
Heart beating frantically,
Everywhere I look,
I am reminded
I am different.

SEX ED

I had my sex education
Two years ago.

I learned how babies are made
With girls.

A banana was peeled,
A condom rolled
Down its length.

We were given booklets
On safe sex,
Pens with funny logos.

Nobody told me
You could be attracted
To boys.

They didn't tell me
What happens
When boys like boys.

They didn't explain
The bulge in my pants
When I saw that man
At the BBQ.

DAD

Dad arrived home today.
I must remember
To be patient
With a man that
Seems
Smells
Sounds
Like my father,
But forgets things easily,
Repeating the same set stories,
Lashing out at his family
On a regular basis.
Mam holds our family together
With octopus arms.
We struggle to adjust.

FAMILY THERAPY

The therapist tells us
We should be honest —
Respect each other.

In a family of talkers
With a zero-patience father,
The loudest.
voice
wins so

We all lose.

We don't listen
To   each other.

Our first and last session.

It's no surprise that
It ends in shouts for attention.

ONE ON ONE

Sonia tells me to relax.
This is a safe space.
Her office is not somewhere
I associate with safety.
We talk about feelings
I'm too young to comprehend:
Anger aimed at my dad
For not trying harder,
Frustration for mam
Who lets my dad
Get away with too much.
The boundary between
Dad and brain injury is
A muddy one.
I know he can try harder.
He has no problem
Drinking himself
Into unconsciousness but
Too sore to walk
To the shop
To buy a newspaper.
Sonia fails to resolve
Deep-rooted issues
With therapeutic words.
She offers me
Group sessions

With peers in similar situations.
I accept,
Figuring it can't be any worse than
This tête-à-tête torture.

GROUP THERAPY

Three girls and
One boy
Sit in a circle,
Framing Sonia.
I take the empty chair,
Listening to their stories,
Absorbing their thoughts,
Processing their feelings.
It feels good
To meet people that
Feel how I feel.
It's my turn —
Words flow from my mouth.
The others nod,
Pat my back,
Smile sadly.
They know what it's like
To live with a parent that
Feels like a stranger.

LYNN

I met Lynn
In group therapy.
We sipped coffees,
Ate burgers and chips
While I waited
For the right moment
To kiss her.

The boys in my class
All kissed girls.
If I kissed a girl,
Maybe I would be like *them*.

We walked through Stephen's Green
Stopping beside the pond
When our lips met,
All tongue and canines:
Confirmation that
I do not like girls.

BREAKUP

We held hands,
Ate in cafes,
Watched movies
But Lynn was
Not affectionate.
Our breakup
Came as no surprise.

MASK

I tried hard
To hide my sexuality
But
A girlfriend did not
Stop the taunts,
Stop the pain
Of being

Different.

CHOICES

We have been given forms,
Choices we must make,
Subjects we must
Carry forward
For our Leaving Certificate:
Exams that will
Shape our futures.

 English

 Maths

 Irish

 French –

All compulsory
But I choose

 Geography

 Biology

 Physics –

Determined to understand
Who I am
How I am
Why I am.

SATISFACTORY

Seasonal report cards arrive,
My English teacher
Reminding me that
I am

Poor
Satisfactory √
Average
Above average
Outstanding

Is that why I am bullied?
Is that why these thoughts
Buzz in my mind?
Why can't I be better?

ACCOMMODATION

They built an extension
Onto our house,
To accommodate dad,
To give him
A bathroom and bedroom
So he could completely

Isolate himself.

CONTROL

I cannot control
The feelings
Whirring through my mind:
Stress about exams,
Worry that I have no friends,
Anxiety about people
Finding out
Who I really am.

THE NIGHT BEFORE

The night before
My first exam.
I cannot sleep.
Cannot eat.

I lie in bed,
Staring at the ceiling,
Wishing this was over.

My first exam:
English.
Deciphering prose,
Interpreting poetry,
Creating stories
Does not come easily
After three years
Of being satisfactory.

EXPECTATIONS

Mam holds my hand
In the car,
A gentle squeeze
Offering reassurance
As my heart
Jackhammers in my chest.
All she wants:
To see me happy.
Just do your best,
She tells me,
As the car door
Slams behind me.

Just d

Just do your best

Just do your b

Just do your best

Just do your best

Just do yo

STRESS

Pain flares
During the exams,
Claiming precious minutes
Of exam time
As I run to the toilet
To alleviate cramps.
Mam warned me
Stress would do this.
How can I
Stay calm?
So much
Rides on these exams.

CELEBRATIONS

The boys celebrate
The end of exams by
Guzzling cheap beer,
Making out with girls,

Bragging,
Bantering.

I sit on my bed,
Staring at my reflection.

FANTASY

I stay in my room,
Jamming thumbs
Onto buttons
On a joystick.

Much easier
To live in a game
Than face the reality
Of my sad life.

JUNIOR CERTIFICATE

English.. C

Irish .... B

Maths.. B

Geography .... B

History.. B

Science.. A

Business Studies .... B

Religious Studies .... A

French.. C

Art... D

SECRET

The pain
In my chest
Dulls
When I see
My results.
A childhood friend
Invites me out
For drinks.
We chat
About exams,
About games,
About everything,
But the unspoken secret
In the back
Of my mind.

BIOLOGY

Biology comes naturally
To me.
It's easy to understand
What makes humans tick.

Mrs Davis passes
My latest exam to me.
An A at the top,
Pride lights her face.

BEAUTY

Three years of being
Satisfactory
Shattered my confidence:
Deciphering poetry,
Weaving stories,
Acting out plays.

Extra tuition,
Study supports,
Revision sessions,
Could not help me
Break through
My inabilities.

Ms Fitzsimons is my teacher now.
She hands me
My poetry assignment,
Discussing beauty
In the unlikeliest of places —
A *B-* catches me by surprise.

MS FITZSIMONS

I wait
For the room to empty
Before I approach her.

Did you make a mistake?
I ask shakily.
No,
She answers without hesitation,
You deserve the grade.
And, she adds,
As I leave the classroom,
You're capable of better.

FORTRESS

Dad does not ask
About school,
About friends,
About me.
He sits inside
His fortress,
Making beers disappear,
Gorging on mammoth meals,

Ignoring the outside world —
The visible pains
Of his two children.

RESOURCES

I am
The only boy
In my year
Studying Honours Physics.
My school,
Short on resources,
Lumps me in
To an all-levels class.
It is difficult
To understand nuclear physics
With ten boys
Throwing paper balls,
Shouting,
Distracting my teacher
With Gaelic football.
Letters and numbers
Swirl across the pages:
Equations I fear
I will never understand.

CENTRAL APPLICATION OFFICE

I make my choices:
For Science courses,
Ranking universities
One to five.
It should be an easy choice so
Why is there a niggling doubt
In the back of my mind?

POPPIES IN JULY

Feather-like,
Fluid,
Free,
Plath's words
Float upon the page,
Entangling nature and pain
In combinations
Most deadly.

Fatal,
Fearsome,
Fiery,
The images
Flicker upon the page —
Red, bloodied mouths,
Poppies alight,
Leaching colour
From my world.

CHANGE OF MIND

Last day
To change my mind,
To alter the direction
Of my future.

Pen to paper,
I breathe deep,
Calm my racing mind
As I choose English
Over Science.

ALWAYS DIFFERENT

From an early age,
I never fit in.
I tried
To play games,
Chat to other boys,
Share lunch
But I was always
Different.

In secondary school,
My best friend
Abandoned me
To a pack of wolves
Without explanation.
My illness just matched
The exterior to the interior,
Connecting dot to dot,
So the world could see
My difference.
I tried so hard to be normal;
To fit in,
Look,
Feel,
Act
Like everyone else.
But my humour,

My tendencies are
An acquired taste that
Some like,
Some loathe and,
Just like my illness,
Some will accept me,
Some will reject me,
But I must learn to love myself
Because I am done with
Fitting in.

ENOUGH

Enough
Of pencil parings
Dropped into my hair,
Of gay slurs
Spat at me,
Of kiss-shaped bruises
On my skin.

Nerve endings fray,
Thoughts fizz in my head,
Cut deeper than skin,
Making me question
My existence.

Enough
Of the toxic peers
Poisoning my life.

Today:
I attend my final classes.
I will not return
Until I sit
The Leaving Cert exams.

GRADUATION LOOMS

I cannot wait
To escape the nobodies who have
Preyed upon me
For the last five years.
I left school early
To study at home,
To be free from bruises and
Names that cut deeper than
Any scalpel.

I attend a meeting today
To discover we need
A robe and hat
For graduation;
A formality that costs mam money yet
Means nothing to me.
Mam never finished school though.
I know this means a lot to her.
I suck it up,
Exhale my fears as
I hold out my hands
While the tailor
Measures my arms.

GOOD TIMES

Shouts and laughs
Pierce the air
As I enter the hall
With mam.
The teachers
Greet students
Who punch each other
On the shoulder.
Recalling the "good times".
I cannot remember those:
Slurs spin through my mind,
Bruises on my body,
Razor-like threats
Pressing against my skin.
Everyone smiles,
Claps,
Beams
But behind it all
I wonder if their parents
Know what monsters
Their 'good boys' are?

GRADUATION DAY

I move across the stage,
Accepting my diploma
From Mr Malone.
I pose for the photo,
Bathing in proud, parent smiles,
Thinking of the good, bad and
Ugly moments that
Paved the path
To this moment.
He holds the awards list
In his small, red hands.
I win
Irish and
Maths Scholar
Since I'm the only
Honours level student
In either class.
I blink,
Open and close my mouth
When he announces
Student of the Year.
I stand,
Holding the plaque
Close to my chest.
My name is etched
On one of the many crests
Adorning it.

I've won medals before
In everyone-is-a-winner
Sports events but
This is different.
I earned this.
Endured the darker moments,
Shined bright enough
To dazzle my teachers.
Mam embraces me,
Dad shakes my hand
When I return to our table.
She has tears in her eyes that
Streak mascara
Down her cheeks.
Teachers congratulate me,
Shaking mam's hands,
Saying what a special student
I am.
I dreaded this moment.
I went for mam but
Now that I'm here,
I want to
Bottle these memories,
Remember the handshakes,
Plug kind compliments into my ears so
I can forever feel this glow.

LEAVING CERT EXAMS

I am worried that
I might blank in the exam;
Misunderstand a question,
Forget a quote.
My biggest worry:
My illness.
What if cramps start?
What if I need the toilet?
What if the adhesions attack?
I cannot control any of this.

NORMAL

I want to be normal.

I don't ask teachers for help.
I don't tell anyone when I'm in pain.
I don't confide in friends.

Magazines
Newspapers
Video games
TV
Movies
Theatre —
All remind me of 'normal'.
1 in 10,000 sets me apart.

My illness is rare,
A wild beast,
Difficult to control and coax
At the best of times.
Normal is unobtainable.

HAVE I DONE ENOUGH...?

My fingers fumble
With the envelope,
Crinkling paper
As they extract
My Leaving Cert results.
The results are good
But not good enough
To stop my racing heart
As one question
Weighs heavy
On my mind:
Have I done enough
To get into college?

LEAVING CERT RESULTS

English.. B

Irish C

Mathematics .... C+

Biology.. B+

Physics .... C+

Geography C

French... C

OFFER

University College of Dublin
Make an offer
To study English.

Without hesitation,
I accept,
Smiling for the first time
In what feels
A lifetime.

FIRST DAY

I fizz with nervous energy
As I bounce from class to class
On my first day
Of college.
I lose myself
Under a mountain of books
In the library,
Explore cavernous lecture theatres,
Lose my way
Every five minutes but
Everyone is friendly,
Guiding me on the right path.
I worry about my illness,
About five hundred students
Hearing cramps that
Sound like hunger pains.
Familiar questions
Bombard my brain
In spite
Of this new experience.

SPANISH

In Spanish class,
I meet Clara:
A sweet girl,
Quiet,
Patient,
Calming,
So unlike me
With deadlines,
Exams,
Essays,
Whirling in my mind.
We sit together
At lunch,
Share stories,
Work on assignments —
So welcoming
To finally have
A friend.

LESSON LEARNED

Faced with my results,
It's clear:
Languages are clearly
Not my forte.
Maybe it's the way they're taught.
Words are something magical
To be experienced —
I'm not sure
Textbook teaching is for me.

DEAD END

Head spinning,
I visit the arts adviser who
Calms me down,
Highlighting how good
I am at English.
She reassures me,
Makes phone calls,
Fires off emails,
Telling me to
Remain calm.
The next day,
She returns
With a solution.

DRAMA STUDIES

Medieval
Renaissance
Victorian
European
Traditional
Contemporary
Experimental
Meant to push the boundaries of
Race
Sexuality
Gender
Class
So much more.
Drama studies is
As natural
As swimming.

APPOINTMENT

I hold mam's hand
As she opens the door.
Dr Deasy stands,
Shakes my hands,
Asks me questions,
Inspects my medical history.
Mam speaks —
I try to follow,
Unable to keep up
With medical jargon:
Anal anastomosis,
Ileo-anal pouch,
Ileostomy,
Pouchitis,
Restorative proctocolectomy.
I do not understand but
Dr Deasy is the best
At what he does.
He operated on mam and
She is healthy.

What do I have
To fear?

SURVIVAL

Mam raves about Dr Deasy:
How good he is,
How nice,
How professional.
Because she had one surgery —
She survived.
At 26
When I started this journey
At 11.
Years bring experience,
Knowledge,
Trust,
But at 11
I was thrown into this

Blind,
Unknowing,
Confused.

But if she survived
Maybe I can too?

PATIENT INFORMATION BOOKLET

I read through
The patient information booklet,
Trying to wrap
My seventeen-year-old mind
Around all of this.
It breaks down
The medical jargon,
Offers FAQs
But none of this
Helps with how I feel.

GOOGLE

Google can tell you | What FAP is   🔍

A genetic disease
Where benign polyps
Will grow in the epithelium
Of the large intestine,
And change
Or take
A life.

Google can tell you | Polyps   🔍

May bleed
Leak into the stool
Lead to anaemia,
Requiring regular colonoscopies
To confirm diagnosis.

Google can tell you | How this will make you feel   🔍

No information is
Available for this page:
Learn why.

It doesn't say
Doctors will bombard you

With medical talk,
Leaving you with little to no idea
What is happening to your body.

Google doesn't say
You'll wear a mask to hide your pain,
Deftly deflect questions
Because you just want to be normal,
To be just like everyone else
But you're not like everyone else.

You're different.
Your scars are etched into your body
For the world to see.

STATISTICS

Statistics never help me sleep.
The odds of
Dying from heart disease: 1 in 6
Dying in a car accident: 1 in 303
Winning big in the lottery: 1 in 13,983,816

My odds of getting FAP are 1 in 10,000
And, somehow,
I managed to win that jackpot.
Better me than my sister?
She erupted into screams
When she had her tonsils removed.
Though they'd never say it,
If one child were to have FAP,
I think mam and dad
Would want it to be me.
Not maliciously;
They know how strong and resilient
I am,
How much of a struggle
It would be for my sister;
A girl who struggles in the world
On the day-to-day,
Navigating a world of
Skinny = pretty
Blonde = slutty

Fat = ugly
I am glad it was me and not her.
I would take this bullet
A thousand times over
If it saved her from this pain.

WOULD YOU TAKE A BULLET ...?

I always found the phrase
Would you take a bullet ...?
A strange one.
A bullet is instant and,
Depending on where it hits,
It can be clean death
Or prolonged agony.
FAP,
On the other hand,
Comes with a wealth of
Physical
Anguish and
Inescapable
Nothingness.
Your mind plays tricks,
Tells you you're not good enough
While adhesions and cramps
Tear through your body,
Leakages make you feel
Like a dirty animal that
Cannot control itself.
Depressed.
Isolated.
Resistant.
Terrified.
Yearning.

You can't show your body
      For fear of ridicule.
         You give up the things you love.
      You take meds that make you
      Constipated.
   Restless.
Apathetic.
Miserable.
Puzzled.
Sedated.
Your mood on the medley of medication
Peaks and plummets like a rollercoaster.
Today could feel a wondrous dream;
Tomorrow, your worst nightmare.
Taking a bullet for someone
Suddenly feels a lot more appealing
Than enduring an illness
Which rules over life
With an iron fist.

ORLANDO

Mam knows how nervous
I am
About my surgeries
So she suggests
A family trip.
I expect Spain or Greece
But I'm amazed when
She says *Orlando*.
My mother did this for me.
My mother always does
Beautiful things for me.

FLIGHT

Flying 35,000 feet in the air,
I am reminded of hospitals,
Of wires running across my waist,
Legs heavy,
Unmoving.

No control over
Tastes,
Sights,
Sounds
Of the everyday,
Flying high
In this aluminium can.

Breathless,
I escape to the toilet,
Bolting it shut.
I stare at the boy
In the mirror,
Wishing I could stop the tears
That swim down his cheeks.

TRAVEL LOVE

I love everything about holidays;
Watching films with my sister and
Gabbling away over the endings,
Eating in-flight snacks,
Gazing out of the aeroplane window
At the tiny people below.

Going to the theme parks,
Splashing in the water —
It never gets old and
That

eXcitement

explodes out of me

Like an erupting volcano.
I can taste candy floss in the air,
Feel sand between my toes,
Hear the waves crash.
Everything is technicolour.
It's not enough
To make me forget
What hangs over me.

CALVIN KLEIN

Mam takes us
To the shopping outlets,
Where we shop
Until we will literally drop.
Shopping is an Olympic sport
In my family
Unless you're my dad,
Who sips beers by the pool.
We start at Calvin Klein
Where I throw shorts and t-shirts,
Boxer shorts and
A leather satchel bag
Into my basket.
I'm shrugging into a t-shirt
In the fitting rooms,
Facing away from the mirror,
From the ugly truth that
Scars me from hip to hip
Like a distorted smiley face.

My arms slide through the fabric.
I'm not staring at the mirror but
The poster,
Of a male model,
Eight-pack,
Glowing skin,
Tall and lean.
A lump in my throat —
My eyes tear up.
I know it's not the end of the world
But my modelling dreams were dashed
When the blood test
Returned a positive result.
I take off the clothes and
Get dressed.
Suddenly,
I don't want these clothes
Anymore.

SPLASHING AROUND

My mother and sister
Splash around in the pool.
I lie on a sunbed,
Covered from head-to-toe
In thirty-eight-degree heat.
The water is lovely,
Mam calls.
I smile and say
I want to relax.
I want to swim
More than anything,
Dive into the water,
Slicing through its coolness
With swift strokes,
Kicking my legs like propellers.
I want to drown my anxieties.
Instead,
I watch and wait
For night to come,
Because like my modelling dreams,
My swimming ones are over.

THE MAGIC KINGDOM

Thundering rollercoasters
Steal breath
From lungs
Sweep negativity
From mind
Banish thoughts
Of illness
Childhood memories
Consume me
Child again
With family

HOMEWARD BOUND

Returning home
Makes the contents
Of my stomach
Feel like drying cement.
The magic
Enshrouding our holiday
Dissipates as we take our seats.
I stare at the black screen,
Wondering when my operation
Will take place.
My stomach churns and cramps.
I'm waiting all over again.
I do not know what's in store,
I do not know when it will come.
The anticipation kills me
Over and over.

HOPE

I submit photos,
Fill out measurements,
Hoping they will accept me,
That my model dreams
May still
Come true.
I stare
At the laptop,
Willing a response,
Knowing what is
To come.

EIREMODELS

A new agency,
A final chance,
A re-ignited dream.

The agency directors
Welcome me
To the Morgan Hotel.

Surrounded by other potentials,
We listen to the professionals:
Make-up artists,
Hairdressers,
Fitness coaches,
Catwalk instructors,
Inspiring us
To grab our dreams
With both hands.

The agency requires a fee
To pay the hotel,
The instructors,
Artists,
Coaches.

Each week,
We learn,
We grow,
We fight
Our way to the top.

SCAM

Mam is the first
To break the news:
Turn on the radio,
Everyone is talking.

I listen,
Praying mam is wrong,
Hoping this is real:
I *need* this to be real.

I feel nauseous
As the news hits me.
Why would anything
Go my way?

All I wanted was
To model,
To feel beautiful
In my own skin.

How is this possible
Now that I know
My modelling dream is
One big scam?

IT

The hot water
Clouds the glass.
With my fingers,
I draw a curve:
A smiley face
Shining back at me.
Water pounds my back.
I look down,
Even in the steam
I see *it*.
Scar stretching
From hip to hip:
Parody of a smile,
Mocking me.
My fingers press
Against my chest,
Moving
Down
Down
Down.
At the last moment,
They skirt around it,
Refusing to see or touch.

MARIAM

The stoma care nurse
Invites me
Into her office,
Removes a booklet
To discuss the surgery.

She tells me
I will have a bag.
While my mind conjures up
Luxury satchels,
She hands me
A beige stoma bag.
It feels odd
Under my fingertips.
She takes the bag,
Showing me how
To attach it,
Empty it,
Change it.
My mind cannot
Take any of this in:
How can this
Be attached to my body?

FINALLY

When the letter
Marking the date
Of my second operation
Finally arrives,
I feel numb.

Slowly,
Feeling filters into my veins and
My world narrows,
My vision blurring.
This is what I waited for.
This is it.
I should be used to this now
But I'm not.
I don't think I'll ever get used
To having FAP.

GIFTS

Mam hands me new bedclothes,
Slippers and towels.
I thank her but she tells me
They're not from her.
Family, friends and neighbours are
Thinking of me,
Will pray for me as I'm wheeled
Down a corridor of bright light,
Into a world of darkness.
I tell mam to thank them and
Hug the pyjamas to my face.
They comfort and calm me.
I wonder if they will comfort me
Post-op,
When I readjust to
A newly disfigured body?

DEJA-VU

Nothing prepares you for
The clinical smell,
Shoes against wet lino that

Squeak,

    Squeak,

        Squeak.

My heart pounds
In my chest
When I see
The 'get well soon' balloons
Floating next to the gift shop.

Sweet and sour smells
Float across the corridor
From the restaurant.
I salivate,
Recalling the pain
Of a week-long fast.

Most of all,
Nothing prepares you
For the people:

Doctors,
Nurses,
Registrars,
Wives,
Husbands,
Sons,
Daughters,
All connected
By sickness and death.
Everyone is somebody's everything.
And somebody's everything is
Inches from Death's door.
Life is such a fragile thing,
I remind myself,
As the nurse
Clasps my name tag
Around my wrist and
Searches for a vein.

THIRST

I long
To wet my lips,
Quench my thirst,
Quell the burning desire
To be held,
To be touched,
To be loved.

STRANGERS

I share this space
With five strangers.
It does not feel appropriate
To prise back the lid
Of their lives,
Poke my nose
Into their business.
The room is spacious
But tobacco-scented breaths
Fill it to capacity.
The men rustle newspapers while
The women chatter.
I keep my fears
Inside my head,
My emotions
In my heart and
My eyes
On my twitching hands.

INSTRUCTIONS

I follow instructions:
Arms straight,
Deep breaths,
Knees to your chest,
Hold it
As long as you can.
The enema burns but
At least it's only one,
Penetrating stubborn muscle.
I lie still
In my bed,
Trying not to move
In case the world
Shifts around me.
I watch other patients
Wolf down hospital food.
Forced to inhale the clouds
Of dry meat that
Waft over to my bed,
I'm ready for this
To be over —
Surgery
Two of three.

THEATRE

When I hear
The nurses talk about theatre,
I think of Beckett and Pinter and
The great contemporary playwrights that
Challenged societal views
On the world stage.
Images race through my mind:
Curtain calls,
Costumes,
Elaborate backdrops,
Powerful dialogue and
Actors that demand your attention.
This theatre is nothing like that but
The scalpel waiting in Dr Deasy's hand
Demands my attention
Much the same.

DR DEASY

I lie in bed,
Staring at doctors and nurses that
Scurry around me —
An anaesthetist preparing his tools,
Nurses checking my vitals,
A doctor inspecting the site.
Seeing Dr Deasy
Feels familiar.
He performed mam's surgery —
I know I'm in safe hands.
I repeat this
To myself.
I shuffle deeper under blankets,
Shutting out the chill that
Sweeps through the theatre.
Dr Deasy asks me about college,
About mam,
About life —
Inane questions that
Help take my mind off
My impending fate.
The anaesthetist slips on the mask,
Turning dials and flicking switches.
I feel my lids grow heavy
As my body caves to sleep.

WHAT'S THIS?

I try to trick my brain:
This is no different
From the last surgery.
My hands numb and heavy,
Wrestle with the blanket,
Struggling to burrow beneath it.
My fingertips graze prickly hair,
Coarse cracked skin,
A papery bulge.
I pull back the blanket,
Examining the beige bag,
Already filled with liquid.
I stare at it,
Horrified yet unable to look away.
Is this my life now?

ROUTINE EFFORTS

Shoes squeak
Against lino floor.
Voices float out of the TV,
Unsuccessful attempts
To distract me
From vicious hunger and
Sharp pains
Like knives
Cutting their way
Out of my belly.
Family and friends arrive
At visiting times:
Routine efforts
To cheer me up.
At night,
Alone,
I bite my nails,
Wondering
Who can protect me
From this suffocation?

CATHETER

Reaching past the dressings that
Cover my skin,
My hand hits a tube
Which I tug at and
Wince.

I look under the sheets.
Urine runs through a tube
From my boxers to a bag
At the side of the bed.

A nurse arrives.
What is it? I ask her.
A catheter, she replies,
Like I should know what that is.

I roll the word around
On my tongue.
It tastes sour,
With hints of sharp glass
Spiking my mouth.

COCKTAIL

nurses inject morphine

into veins

to numb earth-

shattering pai

killing sensation

muffling sounds

of metronomic machines

morphine cracks

open skull sweep

ng o

t

emotion

fear

RIGHT NOW

the only thing

anxiety

keeping jigsaw-puzzle mind

pieced together

FINAL RITES

A spectre hovers beside my bed,
Dressed in brown robes,
Bearing rosary beads.
He touches my forehead —
I recoil.
I close my eyes,
Opening them a crack
From time to time
To check he is gone.
When I see him leave,
I open my bedside drawer,
Feeling for my phone.

I dial mam's number,
Counting down the seconds
Until she answers.
My cheeks are wet,
My vision blurry.

Hello?

I'm dying.

What?

I'm dying, mam.

The priest came
To give me my final rites.

I cannot hear
Her comforting words,
Under the weight of tears that
Burst from my eyes.

HALLUCINATIONS

High doses of morphine
Mess with my mind.

Mam's red-rimmed eyes
Watch me wearily
For hallucinogenic signs
While the last of the morphine
Flows through my veins.

Pain blazes across my belly
When I
Breathe,
Speak,
Stir.
The substitute drugs
Curb the pain,
Unlike morphine which
Obliterated it,
Obliterated self-control
Over body and mind.

MOTHER-SON TALK

Mam sits by my bed
As the morphine wears off.
How are you feeling?
Fine,
I lie through a cotton mouth.
When I had my surgery,
They told me not to eat.
I snuck a piece of cheese
Off the food trolley.
Know what happened?
I shake my head
From side to side –
The room spins.
I look at the middle
Of my three mams.
They forced a tube
Down my throat,
Pumped my stomach.
Oh,
I reply,
Realising
This is her way
Of telling me not to eat
Until they tell me to.
I won't eat the cheese.

Mam laughs,
Rubbing circles
Into the palm of my hand.

BLACK HOLE

The scar is infected.
Instead of a neat line,

I now have a gaping hole

That the nurses tell me
Must be dressed
Every day
By a call-out nurse
When I am discharged.
I tune out after that,
Wincing as a nurse pokes strips of silver
Into the infected insides
Of my body.
I have no idea
How deep it runs
But I pray that it heals neatly.

STOMA

Today,
They change the ileostomy bag.
It stinks.
I'm unsure if it will always
Smell this bad
Or if it's three days
Of liquid sustenance
Administered through drips that
Makes it slosh up the side,
Weigh so heavy that
It peels away from the skin.

The nurse pulls back the bag,
Asking me to gently
Press a wad of cotton pads
Against the stoma.
I oblige as
She unpeels the adhesive
On a new bag,
Tearing open the cleansing wipes.
She takes the cottons pads,
Disposing them.

The stoma is
Red,
Raw,

Tender.
There will be no hiding it.
It looks like an alien's mouth,
Gurgling away as the nurse
Cleans the skin around it which
Stings and itches.

My stomach grumbles
In protest
At the sight.
She cleans it,
Telling me that
I will be doing this soon.
I wonder how I'll clean something that
I can't stand the sight of.

BREATHING EXERCISES

It hurts to laugh,
To cough,
To cry.
If I breathe too deep,
Too long,
It's like a whetted knife
Twisting around,
Turning my insides into spaghetti.

I need to practise
Breathing again.
I'm given
Breathing apparatus;
Three green balls
Positioned in three clear pillars,
Connected by a tube
Which I'll breathe into.
Exhale
Inhale
For as long as you can.
One ball should rise —
That's easy.
The second is a little harder and
The third, harder again.
Take your time, she tells me,

But I want to do this now;
I want to be normal faster.
I do as I'm instructed:

Breathe out,

Breathe out

Breathe in,

Breathe in

But no ball rises.
I'm told to try
Again and again.
And I do —
I do.
I sink my head in shame.
I must practise.
I put the device in the back
Of my bottom drawer.
I do not wish
To be reminded of my failure.

Breathe in

Breathe in

Breathe out

Breathe ou

athe out

PRAYERS

People offer me prayers
When I beg for a welcoming ear;
Compassion to understand
What I have,
Why I endure it.

Cards line the length of my bed;
Christian iconography in place of compassion
Amongst a sea of watchful eyes.

They can walk away from this,
Close the door and forget me.
I can't walk away
From my illness.

GOOD INTENTIONS

Good intentions do not
Make this easier.

Cadbury creme eggs will not
Extract poisonous polyps
From bowels.

Lucozade will not dress
The wounds left behind
In the wake of surgery.

Prayers to a God
No longer believed in
Will not take away pains.

Good intentions do not
Make this easier.

BURNING THROUGH MY INSIDES

The nurse puts on her gloves —
A loud smack
Of rubber against fleshy wrist.
She tells me she will remove my catheter.
Will it be painful?
I ask.
Uncomfortable,
She replies.
She
pulls —
A pain sears
through my insides.

She tells me to press the bell
If I need assistance
But I cannot voice my pain.
I'm not sure there is much
She could do,
Even if I could.

DAM

I walk carefully to the bathroom
With my IV drip wheeling beside me.
I untie my gown and
Hunker down on the toilet seat,
Wrinkling my nose against the stench
Of clinical disinfectant
Warring with years
Of shit and vomit.
I feel urine building in my bladder,
Pressing down on it like concrete.
I wait five minutes but
Nothing comes.

I return to my bed
Defeated.

QUESTIONS

Mam alerts the nurses
Who question me:
Are you really trying?
Could you try again?
Are you sure you can't go?
Of course I'm trying,
I'm sure I can't go and
I would love to try again but
The twenty-step walk
Turns my world upside down.

A specialist is called.

SPECIALIST

The specialist asks considered questions
Where the nurses did not.
She carries out tests,
Ensuring she has covered
All bases
Before making her decision.
I'm in too much pain
To understand what's happening.
I watch as she injects
Clear liquid into my IV drip.
I wait for it to take effect
But the wall of pressure builds.
Curled up in a ball,
Hands tangled in the sheets,
I

      w a i t

An eternity

BLOOD

I squat on the toilet seat.
I'm sure I will piss,
I can feel the pressure
Crushing my body.
I count to ten:
One, two, three...
I suck a deep breath
Through my lips.
Five, six, seven...
Sigh.
Eight, nine, ten...
Push.
Scrunch up my eyes.
Something splatters into the toilet.
It's not urine;
It's warm,
Thicker.
It hurts
To expel it
From my body.
Blood.
Darker than the blood
Flowing through the tube that
Confirmed my illness.
I watch the stain,
Spray-painted onto the clean white

Of the toilet bowl.
I pull the cord
Next to the toilet,
Summoning a nurse.
I show her the blood,
Shuddering.
She does not seem worried
Though it's not her body,
Not her illness.
A wave of fear
Hooks deep under my skin.

SPITTING IN THE FACE OF NORMAL

Blood
Is
Normal,
They explain.

Normal:
I have
No
Idea
What
It
Is
Anymore.

This illness,
My life,
Spits
In the
Face
Of
Normal.

SAHARA THIRST

Mam holds the straw
To my cracked bleeding mouth.

The nurses have allowed me
To wet my lips.

The other patients
Guzzle their dinners around me.

I gargle the water around my mouth,
Wetting my Sahara tongue.

I spit into the empty basin
Mam holds by my side.

MIND RACING

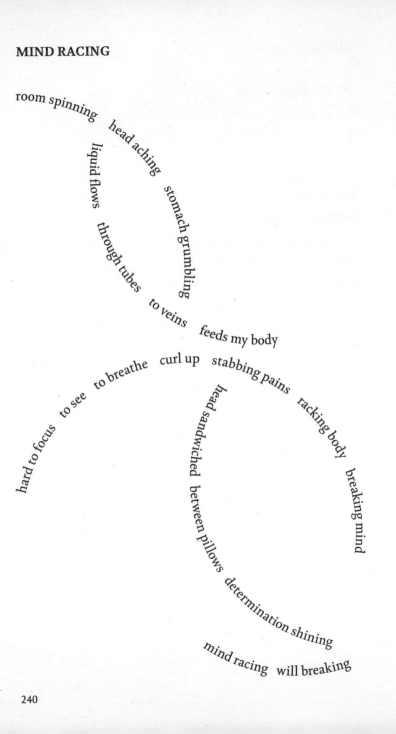

room spinning   head aching   stomach grumbling   liquid flows   through tubes   to veins   feeds my body   curl up   stabbing pains   racking body   breaking mind   to breathe   to see   hard to focus   head sandwiched   between pillows   determination shining   mind racing   will breaking

BANQUET

The catering assistant arrives
With two slices
Of toasted white bread.
My predatory eyes
Home in on my prize.
Too impatient
To fiddle with plastic butter cartons.

I bite into the toast,
Relishing its crispness.
It's only bread but
A week without food
Makes bread
A banquet.

EMPTYING MY BAG

Mariam arrives
All sunshine smiles.
I'm happy to see a familiar face
But dread hardens my stomach:
This is not a social call.

Time to learn
How to empty your bag.
She unpacks:
An ileostomy bag,
Antibacterial wipes,
Cotton pads.

Following her guidance,
I peel back the bag,
Gagging on the foul stench that
Overwhelms my senses.
The red stoma
Demands my attention
Even though I'd rather
Look anywhere else.

I soak up the foul mess
Using cotton pads,
Wipe the skin clean
With antibacterial wipes.

My skin itches uncontrollably.

The stoma can spew –
You need to be quick.
She explains.
I unpeel the adhesive,
Fixing it around the stoma,
Pressing it down,
Pushing it in place.

MENU

I receive a menu
Every afternoon,
Of what I can and cannot eat.
A menu full of
Fruits and vegetables
Feels like a cruel joke
When you have
An ileostomy bag,
With undigested vegetables

Forcing their way
Through your stoma.

MASHED POTATOES AND CHIPS

Today.
The catering assistant notices that
My food is untouched
Again.
He asks me why;
I want to ask him
If he knows anything
About the patients he caters for
But bite my lip.
My mother explains for me.
He asks me what I will eat,
Agreeing to deliver
Mashed potatoes and chips.
Tomorrow.

CONTRABAND

I almost crack a tooth
On the chips and
The potatoes must have
Been mixed with sand.
I pull hard on my mam's heartstrings,
Telling her that she needs
To bring contraband food
To my bed.
She resists but
By the end of her visit,
I've shattered
Her resistance.

WITHOUT

Six days without food,
Without water.

Tubes in my groin,
My wrist,
My arm,
My nose.

Makes me

IMPATIENT
Irritable
Indignant.

Scratchy blankets,
Hazy mind,
Drugs conjuring hallucinations.

I COMPLAIN,
Command,
COAX.

Mam caves,
Driving thirty minutes
To Pizza Hut.

MORE MEDS

I stare at the pills;
Grass green,
Vivid violet,
Bold blue,
In tiny tubs,
Reminding me
Of sweet shop jars.
Bitter sherbet,
Crunchy jazzies,
Tangy cola bottles:
Colours transport me
To my past,
To two-a-penny sweets.
But the tablets
Leave a chalky taste
In my mouth,
Nothing like the
Sweet flavours
Of my past.

MAM

Mam and I
Fight like cat and dog
But we love each other.
We just can't live together
Under the same roof.
I can talk to
My friends,
My sister,
My family,
About most things
But nobody understands
My illness quite like mam,
Who lives it.
I've had it all my life.
Just when I think
I've seen it all,
My stool will discolour,
I'll get a different pain,
I'll feel dizzy.
Symptoms recur and repeat,
Sometimes,
New ones emerge.

When that happens,
I feel so low
Hiding under the covers.
Mam is there,
Holding my hand
As tears wet my pillow.

KINDRED SPIRITS

A lifeline ——————— A heart
Keeping me ——————— Beating
Moving forward ——————— In time
In the world ——————— Around me
Her heart ——————— Anchors me
Here ——————— Momentarily
In stronghold hugs ——————— In make-everything-better kisses
She thinks ——————— Like me
Like me ——————— She loves

WALKING PHARMACY

I lay my meds out
On my bed,
Transfixed by
Shapes and colours.

Green and purple capsules,
Shaped like submarines:
8-12 tablets daily.

White circles
Tasting of cotton candy:
Take when needed.

White torpedoes
Clog my throat:
Take when needed.

A wealth of drugs
Buying me life.

THE WHITE TORPEDOES

The white torpedoes:
30mg Codeine Phosphate Hemihydrate
500mg Paracetamol.

They go by many names:
Zapain,
Kapake —
Names that sound like spaceships
Of some alien species.
Whimsical.
Lyrical.
Novel.

Warned by my doctor,
Warned by my mother:
These are opiates;
Be careful
When and where
You take them.

Bitter taste on my lips,
I push them into my mouth,
One by one,
Banging fist
Against chest
To ease passage
As they prod my gullet.

Now,
It's anyone's guess
When they will
Drag me under —
When I sleep,
It will be near impossible
To fight off Sleep's
Death-like hold on me.

OBLIVION

Nothing:
It creeps up,
Seeps into bone,
Poisons blood.
When it strikes,
Nothing matters.

Nothing:
Can hurt me
More than my own mind,
Twisting everything
Into something
It is not.
I cannot escape.

AFTERMATH

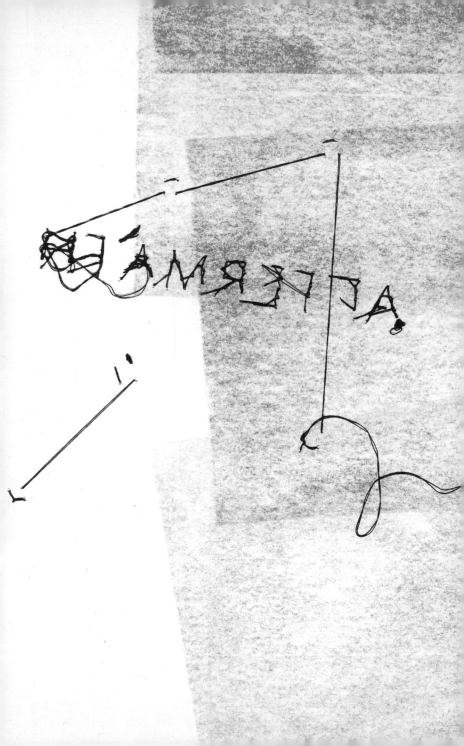

HOME

Pulling into the driveway
Of our house
Conjures mixed feelings.
I'm home but
Still need to
Have the wound dressed,
Be careful what I eat,
Take my meds at set times,
Empty and change
The bag.
Another surgery
Looms on the horizon.
I open the cupboards,
Examining all the food
I cannot eat.
It's hard to look
On the bright side.

MANACLE

The name tag
Hangs around my wrist,
Clamping my fate —
A constant reminder of
What I *have* been through,
What I *am* going through,
What I *will* go through.
I will return to the hospital soon,
For the final surgery:
The ileostomy reversal.
The scissors hover mid-air
Over the tag,
Unsure whether to
Make the cut.

NOT THE END

Mam answers the door.
A smiley nurse with
Bouncing wiry hair
Greets us.

In my bedroom,
She lays out
Strips and dressings,
Chit-chatting
Like she can sense
My firefly nerves.

I bite down on my lip;
Forceps dig into the wound
Driving silver strips
Deep into the infection.

All done, she trills,
Pressing down on the adhesive bandage.
She is wrong.
This is not the end.

SILVER

Silverlon packing strips are
Lodged deep into wound,
Forceps probing under skin.
I count the seconds
Until this is over.
Silver has antibacterial properties but
It will not give me
A neat straight-line scar
Like mam's.
I shudder,
Thinking about
The pus-soaked strips that
Will be removed
Tomorrow.

CRAMPS

Doubled over,
Unable to move,
People brush past me
On the busy Dublin streets.
They ease
For now.
I stride quickly,
Eager to arrive
At my destination
Before they start up again,
Limiting movement,
Maximising pain.

SNOW

Huddled on the windowsill,
I take in a seldom-seen sight:
Soft-to-the-touch snowflakes
Floating down onto muddy ground
Until beauty
Blankets everything.

Brown and green
Turn to white.
Still,
Snowflakes glide down to the ground.
I jump up,
Run to the front door,
Bounding into snow
Up to my ankles.
I let myself slip back.
The snow pillows my fall.

I swipe my arms

Up   Down
Up   Down
Up   Down

My legs swing

In	Out
In	Out
In	Out

I admire my work,
In a blizzard
Of snowflakes.
The crisp air
Chills my face.
Nothing else matters —
Not my bag,
Not my scars.
The snow doesn't judge
As it invites me to play
In a sea of undulating white.
I close my eyes,
Tilting my head to the sky,
Coat covering my bag,
Snowflakes melting on my skin.

DIFFERENT BEGINNINGS

This is the beginning of
Different;
Being judged,
Not ticking boxes and
Looking like everyone else.

This is the beginning of
All my fears;
Years of wanting to fit in at school,
Being given flashing lights
To attract the attention
Of everyone around me.

I do not like this –
Not one bit.

SELF-REFLECTION

I gaze into the mirror:
It's no big deal.
I see a face,
No longer familiar.

From the side,
A normal boy,
Like any other.

From the front,
A vacuum:

Focal point
For dark thoughts.

HYDRA

In the mirror,
My scar reminds me of
A hydra
When it shows
Its many heads.
A tiny cavern,
Hollowed out of flesh:
I shiver,
Body shrouded
In my nightgown.
Pain,
Cramps,
Adhesions,
24-pills-a-day routines,
Make me wish my life away.
Dark thoughts creep up on me
Like a shadow
At bedtime,
Breathing condensation onto windowpanes,
Filtering through window cracks.
The voice of the hydra has
Claws inside me.
Never
Letting
Go.

SHAVING

The stoma itches,
Liquid burning skin,
Tiny hairs chafing.
I lay out fresh supplies:
Ready to clean the skin,
Shave new hairs that will
Make the stoma
Red,
Swollen,
Hot.
I remove the bag carefully,
Liquid sloshes inside.
I work fast,
Careful not to cut myself.
I sweep antibacterial wipes
Around it,
I pull back the adhesive,
On a fresh bag,
Placing it over the stoma,
Seconds before today's dinner
Spurts into the bag.

18

Now that I am 18,
Lisa has convinced me
To go out,
Drink my first pint of beer and
Dance with boys.

Despite
Flashing lights,
Pounding beats,
Gyrating bodies,
I cannot get over
The ileostomy bag that
Churns beneath
My XL t-shirt.

I scratch my belly
Highlighting the line of the bag.
Has anyone seen it?
It feels heavy,
Adhesive tearing against
Hairs that grow fast
Around my belly,
Tickling and itching.

I make my way to the furthest cubicle,
Lock the door.

Empty the bag,
Gagging at the smell.
I tear tissue,
Pressing it to the stoma,
Discard the bag.
The stoma spews
Brown-yellow liquid
Into the tissue.
I reach for the toilet roll but
Liquid spills
Onto my jeans.

Holding my breath,
I wait for the spewing to stop.
Has anyone heard?
I wait a beat,
Before applying the new bag.

I undress,
Donning fresh clothes.
Tucking the bag into my elasticated chinos.
I wrap the old bag in a plastic bag,
Tucking it into my rucksack.
Does anyone smell it?
I exit the cubicle
Not looking back

As I take Lisa's hand and
Leave.

I should not have come tonight.
I do not look like everyone else.
I do not belong.

IN THE TAXI

I take in a city of bright lights and
Brighter possibilities.
All this could have been mine –
Right now,
It's hard to see any light
In my future.

BAG OF SHIT

gurgle

Emptying your ileostomy bag
In the nightclub bathroom
Packed with young handsome men is
Not the best plan for seduction.

gurgle

Yellow kernels *plop, plop, plop*
I ate corn; the bag gurgles it up.
An uncomfortable pressure swells
Around the stoma when the
kernels pass though.

gurgle

I feel as sexy as a slug
Sliming across walls.
I clean the opening,
Tuck the bag
Out of sight.

plop

plop

plop

DIET

At the supermarket,
I sweep through aisles,
Avoiding fibre
That would pass through my system.
Cramps limit my options:
Bananas,
Potatoes —
Anything else will
Confine me to bed.
Avoiding herbs,
Wholegrain
Wholewheat —
Wholesome,
Not for me.
My diet is minimal
In a world
That processes food
Into packaging,
Fortified with fibre,
Threatening me with
Pressing pains.

BASE URGES

At the train station,
I search frantically
For a toilet.
My eyes light up
When I see a sign –
Despairing at
Twenty-cent admission.

How can I pay
With no cash in my pockets?

I sit on the floor,
Press my back against the wall,
Push folded arms on my belly
To counter
Persistent pains,
Inhaling,
Exhaling.
Tears prick the backs of my eyes.
I bring knees to chest
Trying desperately to disguise
The cramps.

SURVIVAL

Navigating college is
A different game
With an ileostomy bag.
Sitting close to toilets,
Monitoring meals,
Organising medication —
Just some of the things
I need to do
To survive.

MAGIC AND MYTH

Harry Potter —
I'm lost to a world of magic and myth —
A world of spells and butterbeer,
Friendship and foes.
I've waited months for this lecture.
My wrist throbs
As pen scrawls across paper.
With a grumble,
My bowel cramps
Across my lower abdomen,
Like earthquake tremors,
Pain worsens
With each wave.
Pen hits the floor
As I sweep books
Into my bag,
Unable to pick them up.
Contorted by pains,
I wait for it to ease
Before darting up the stairs,
Sprinting to the toilet.

DEMENTOR

Under the unforgiving Sun,
I don a faux-fur coat,
Designed for thickset men,
To conceal the bag.

I left the lecture
But, here,
In the tutorial,
I can hear what I missed.

It's hard to focus —
A Dementor on the fringes
Like a barrier
To the magic of Harry Potter.

I imagine the bag,
A heartbeat of its own,
Pulsating beneath
A dark cloak.

Hope pervades me,
Echoes of what has happened,
Engulfing the present,
Portents of what is to come.

LATE FOR A LECTURE

Late!
A text flashes:
Where are you?

I don't reply.
The bag is off,
The stoma spewing
Today's lunch.

I tear tissue
From the roll,
Dabbing corn-peppered mulch
From my chinos.

At least they're brown, I think,
Unable to neutralise the scent of shame.
A knock on the door:

Hurry the fuck up!

I turn and catch my elbow.
I curse,
Taking a wet wipe,
Cleaning the stoma.
This red piece of my bowel
Disgusts me.

I am repulsed by my body.
Another knock.
A wave of panic.

I need a fucking piss.

I press the new bag,
Firmly around the stoma.
Counting to ten,
Relieved by the fresh plastic smell.

I wrap the soiled bag
Double knotting plastic.
Unbolting the door,
I dread the reaction.

What the fuck is that?

Side-stepping,
I lower my head,
Not wanting to meet his eyes.

THEY

What do you do
When they
Whisper,
Laugh,
Sneer
At you,
At your bag,
At your scars —
Unrelenting assaults
For being
Who you are?
What do you do
When they

Stare,

Point,

Judge

Something
You hope
They will never
Experience?

I don't know
Who they are,
What they want,
Why they do this,
But I need to be
Stronger than them,
More tolerant,
More patient
With people
Who have
No idea
Who am I.

POO

They stare at you like
An animal in the zoo
For something
As natural,
As necessary,
As poo.
Social taboo but
Nothing new so
Why do you jeer and jibe
When I use the loo?
Especially when you poo, too.

FIRST CRUSH

Something about him
Magnetises me.
He glides around campus,
Cool,
Carefree,
Confident.
In groups,
He ignores me,
Refusing to make eye contact.
Sam's silence
Makes me
Want him
Even more.

INVITE

Tanya tells me
There is a party,
That I should come.
I touch my fingers
To the inflated bag.
She bulldozes
Through my protests.
I'll see you at 7.
Sam will be there.
She knows what to say

To tempt me.

PARTY

I popped two
Codeine tablets and
Skipped dinner.
I will not embarrass myself
In front of Sam.
Tanya links arms.
We march through campus,
Entering suburbia,
When Tanya stops,
Knocking on a red door.

SAM

Sam opens the door,
Beer in one hand,
Pulling Tanya close
With the other.
Come in.
He gestures
To Tanya.
I follow,
A shadow
Before she introduces me.
You remember Chris?
Sam nods half-heartedly,
Chugs his beer.
Music booms from the kitchen,
Girls shouting,
Telling me their names.
I sip a beer,
Aware that too much
And the gas will
Inflate my bag.
I came for Sam
But he doesn't
Speak to me,
Look at me,
Smile at me.
My heart sinks,

Unsure why I came,
Unsure who I am.
Unsure what I want.

MIDNIGHT

I want
To be seen
To be touched
To be heard
But, instead,
I'm in the corner,
Listening to inane chatter.
Sam disappeared out back
With the guys.
I am not
One of the guys.
I am gay.
I cannot join them.
I stay with Tanya,
With the girls.
I check my phone —
A nervous tick.
It's midnight already.
It begins
To dawn on me:
We have no way home,
No night bus.
We are here
For the night.

WITCHING HOUR

Beer has made
The boys tired.
They leave
Together
With the girls
While Tanya and I
Crash
In the spare bedroom.
I hear a bang
Downstairs.
I follow the sounds,
Fighting my better judgement.
In the living room,
Sam sits in his boxers,
Looking at me,
Seeing me,
Calling me.
Tanya will never
Believe me
But, finally,
It all makes sense:
Sam is gay.

COUNTRY BOY

I have no way
To know,
No way
To be certain.
Sam is
A country boy.
He knows I am gay,
Will not come close
In case I discover.
Beneath his mask,
I see him,
See his pain.
I pretend to forget,
Do not speak a word.
I watch
Knowing I should not pry,
But unable
To help myself.

FOCUS

Deadlines loom,
Essays due,
Exams approach —
Quotes to learn,
History to check,
Research to aim
For top marks.
This should be
My focus but
Instead,
I
Check the stoma,
Change the bag,
Limit my diet.

TAKE TWO

I apply the bag
Around the stoma.
No one has banged down the door
Or shouted and ridiculed me.
I feel safe.
A gentle

t-a-p   t-a-p   t-a-p

On the door.
I wash my hands.
Unlock the door.
A woman in a wheelchair glares.
Why are you using this toilet?
She shouts,
Thinking her need is above mine.
You *can't* see some disabilities.
People stare.
I feel their eyes but
They do not see.
I mumble apologies,
Biting hard on my lip.
Persecuted on two fronts,
I retreat to the fifth floor
Of the library:
A sanctuary
From others.

MY DISABILITY

I have a disability.
Why can't I
Say this
Out loud?

I don't want to be
Looked down on
But have needs
That no one sees.

I don't want to be
Treated differently
For something
Others don't understand.

When I talk about disability
My opinions are less.
I am dismissed
Because my legs and arms work.

I am not disabled:
Society tells me,
My friends tell me.
I hide my disability from the world.

They cannot know,
What they do not see.

I AM DIRTY

The white torpedoes
Pull me under,
Into a drowsy semi-sleep
Where nightmares surface
To torture and torment.
I wake,
Feeling my boxers,
Repulsed by the leakage
Seeping onto the sheets.
I hurry to the bathroom,
Stepping into the bath,
Removing my boxers.
With the shower hose,
I clean the mess
Running down my legs.
My tablets do not
Always work.
On these nights,
I am dirty.

HIGH FASHION

Which ileostomy bag will
I choose today?
I pull back the hangers,
Fingering the fabric,
Admiring the lengths and
Fifty shades of beige.
I make my choice —
All the while,
Examining my stoma in
A funhouse mirror.

ANCHORS

Family and friends
Anchor me to this moment.
Winds rage.
Stormy seas weaken my resolve;
Dark clouds loom on the horizon.
Through it all,
I hold mam's hand,
Hug my sister,
Chat with friends,
Reminding myself that
Dozens of bright moments will
Fend off the darkness.

BLACK HOLES

I'm alone
In the shower:
My body,
The bag.
I wash around it,
Unable to touch it.
It consumes me,
Its papery material,
The smells –
Reminding me
Of my abnormality,
My body is bloated,
Wide hips reaching out
To shower walls.
Water thuds
Against the tiles
Like bullets.
Above it all,
I still hear the stoma,
Churning liquid
Into the ileostomy bag.

What's that on your belly? Can you smell that? Hurry up in there! Big hips! Black hole.

STANDARD PROCEDURE

I'm nervous.
It's a standard procedure
To reverse the ileostomy but
Clinical smells,
Beeping monitors,
Blue scrubs,
Bring back memories
I want to forget.

SCREAMS

A patient screams,
Pulling tubes
From her body,
Flooding the floor with
Blood and urine.

I swipe across my phone,
Desperate for a distraction
From alarming nights and
Exhausting days.

Twisting and turning,
Tubes wrap around my body
Like vines,
Choking me.

The only thing
That keeps me sane is
The ping of a message
From my first crush.

A volcano of happiness
Erupts inside me,
Eclipsing the screams,
Dissolving anxiety.

GLOW

We talk about nothing.
We talk about everything.
When I sleep at night,
No one can steal my glow.

THE DARK KNIGHT

All my deadlines
At university
Have been extended.

For performance studies,
I chose my essay title
To match my favourite movie.

'Dark play
In *The Dark Knight*'
Has a poetic ring to it.

Part-entertainment,
Part-study,
I take notes.

I lie in bed,
Watching *The Dark Knight* –
Cinematic genius.

ASSIGNMENT

I have watched
The Dark Knight
Three times
This week.

Progress to date:
Three words —
Film title.

I should be worried but
The pain meds make me sleepy,
Too groggy to do much and
Too sleepy to care.

ROMANTIC DAYDREAMS

A gondola down
The Venetian canals,
Sipping champagne,
Hands clasped tightly:
Together.

Soft floral scents
Of tulip fields,
Luring us into comfort
In Amsterdam:
Blissful.

Afternoon tea with
Colourful cakes,
Flavourful tea,
In the heart of London:
Idyllic.

These thoughts consume me
Amidst disinfectant burning my nose,
Cardboard food choking me,
Patient cries and beeping monitors
Keeping everyone
Alive.

WALK

Supported by mam,
The nurses let me walk
To the hospital entrance.
We wait for the lift,
Watching the numbers light up
One after the other:

1

2

3

4

Our arms hooked
At the elbow,
We enter the lift.

4

3

2

1

The downward motion
Makes my stomach lurch
But I quickly recover.
At the rotating entrance,
A breeze ruffles my gown,
Refreshing me with its coolness.

TEMPTATION

I am finally allowed to eat
Chocolates and cakes,
Fizzy drinks and jellies,
Gifts from visitors.
Two days without food is
Nothing when you've
Gone a week without
Water.
The nurses warn me
Not to gorge myself,
Not to make myself sick.
My system cannot handle excess.
The temptation to shovel
Jelly babies down my throat is
Tantalising but I resist,
Understanding that
A pumped stomach will not be
A pleasant experience.

HOME ISN'T SAFE

I am home,
But home isn't safe –
Not a place
Where I can feel free.
My bedroom:
Windows and walls,
Mirrored wardrobes
Facing my bed.
A constant reminder
Of my difference.

MIRROR

The mirror distorts truth,
Its clear exact surface,
Tells everything
You never wanted to know
And more.

With finger and thumb,
I probe my healing wound.
Red and raw —
I'm hopelessly optimistic that
It might close,
But the wound
Sucks in all
Positive thoughts.

I judge its appearance
From the side,
Noting how it looks like
A shark's bite,
Yet to be treated.

I never want to
See it,
Touch it,
Feel it
Again.

BUTCHERED

I pinch the sides of my belly,
Inhaling until I see my ribs,
It does not matter how good I look —
The scar still distorts my body,
A parody of a chess board.
What is the point in
Working out
When even I will not look
At this butchered body?

SNAKES AND LADDERS

My entire life feels like
A weighted game
Of snakes and ladders:
A python consumes me whole,
Crushing bones.
Everyone around says
Cheer up,
But it's not that easy to flick
A switch that you cannot find.

I slide Down Down Down

I AM NOT OK

It's the feeling inside
That I'm not me anymore,
That my body —
Not mine.
That my thoughts —
Not mine.
That my feelings —
Not mine.
If that's the case:
Who am I?
What is this empty shell that's
Lost everything it loves,
Watched dreams burn to ashes,
Stared through a telescope at
A love it will never have?
If I cannot
Exorcise these demons from my mind,
How can I find the energy to live,
To own this pain,
To wake in the morning,
Act like I'm fine as
Everyone expects?
Anxiety isn't just
Nerves and panic attacks,
Not something that can be
Wished away with small white circles.

I am not OK.

PLASTIC

What seems to be the problem?
The doctor asks.

I want surgery
To cover my scar,
I reply,
Voice weak.

You don't need surgery.
You can hardly see it.

He points to my belly
Where I see a black hole
Capable of ingesting
Planets and stars.

I stand up straight,
Catch his eye:
I cannot look at myself in the mirror
Or do the things I love to do
Because I hate how I look.

We wait for what feels an eternity,
Before he tells us:

I will schedule an appointment
With a plastic surgeon.
It could take a year.

A year —
Can I tolerate this
For a whole year?

IRON MAN

Feeling fatigued,
Light-headed,
Appearing pale,
Sleeping sporadically,
Concentration low with
Pulsing headaches.

Keeping my eyes open
During lectures:
A momentous effort.
Standing on the bus:
Everything spins.
Twelve-hour sleeps:
Still exhausted.

Early on,
I'm diagnosed with anaemia.
They give me tablets that
Make my stool black
Like tar.
They tell me to take
Vitamin C,
To drink forbidden orange juice;
Ignorant of earth-shattering pains
Following fibrous food and drink.

JUICED

Red tablets
The size of rhinestones
Spill across the counter.

Blood red and menacing,
They will help my anaemia,
Stop me feeling weak.

No one told me about
The twenty toilet trips each day,
The agonising pains.

Hard to believe
Something so small,
So pretty
Could produce stools
Black as night.

SEEN

My bag is gone,
Stoma inside me,
But the same thoughts
Spiral in my mind.
My eyes dart
Around the club,
At guys
Peering at me.
I swig my beer,
Flashing lights and
Pounding beats,
Wondering if they see me?
Has anyone ever really
Seen
Me?

TITANIC

I always wanted
Someone to hold me
The way Jack holds Rose
In *Titanic*.
I wanted fairy-tale romance,
Disney kaleidoscopic colour,
Symphonic songs.
Someone to hold me tight;
Someone to do that for me
When I couldn't love myself.

THE IDEAL

I always thought
Gay dating would be easy.
Man + man = the ideal.
No unwanted pregnancy,
No baby bumps.
Just fun and frolics
Between the sheets:
Hand holding
Sprinkled with hold-me-closer hugs.
It wasn't like that for me.
I learned early that
Me + man = complicated.
A man needs to meet his beau –
In a jigsaw-puzzle world,
That means every top
Needs a bottom.
My illness imposes
my role:
Top.

TOPS AND TURVY

Ben showed me
Around Dublin:
Vintage bars,
Cool coffee shops,
Artsy films that
Changed the way
I saw the world.
When he held my hand,
My cheeks glowed —
Butterflies fluttered
Against my belly,
Desperate to escape.
He made me feel wanted,
Loved,
Everything I always needed
From a relationship,
From a boy.
It killed me
When we learned
We were both tops,
When the light in his eyes
Switched off.
I never saw him again.

TOPS AND BOTTOMS

Demonstrating sex ed
Between man and woman is
Easily done with a banana and donut.
With two men,
The discussions become
A little more complex.
Some boys sleep
On the top bunk and
Others on the bottom bunk.
Some guys sleep in
Both bunks depending
On mood and on man.
Diagnosed with FAP,
The decision was never mine.
The top bunk is my bed
Whether I like it or not.

CURTAIN CLOSE

It's a funny thing
When you meet
A boy you'd gladly give
Your heart to.
Sweaty palms,
Cheek-to-cheek grins and
Lying side by side
All feel like big wins
When he whispers
In your ear
How much he cares
About you;
How much he sees an 'us'
In him and you.
It makes you stop,
Wonder how you got so lucky,
How you got to this
Incredible place with an A+ guy
Who loves you
Up until
Curtain
Close.

DATING

Dating is a funny beast
That I have never tamed.
Being told you're face-value pretty
And having someone cherish
Your inner and outer beauty is
Something else entirely.

A picture on the web,
Three lines of text
Tells them my life story
But it doesn't tell them that:

I go to the bathroom between
Ten and twenty-five times a day.

I get adhesions that
Tear my body inside out
With agonising pain.

Leakages are not uncommon
But most unwelcome.

I am limited in what I can eat,
What I can drink.

OUT ON THE TOWN

Night out on the town
I've OD'ed on codeine
To avoid the anxieties
Of the men's toilets:
Broken door locks,
Empty toilet roll dispensers,
Guys that laugh and look
Like you're an animal
At the zoo.
Anxiety aside,
There are still cramps,
Twisting me into pretzel shapes
Whenever I drink.

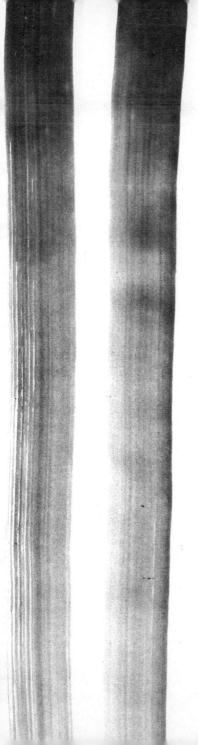

CODEINE CODE

Shapes shift
Under a sleepy half-stare.
Lids like liquid concrete
Weigh down my eyes
Against my will.
Words enter one ear and
Float out of the other.
I cannot comprehend anything
When white torpedoes
Work through my veins,
Muddying my mind.
To the world around me,
I am uninterested,
Uncaring,
Uninvolved.
This is not
Of my own volition.
Fear spikes:
Short-lived,
Short-term.
Nothing can compete with that
Siren song,
Pulling me under,
Into a world where
Only nightmares can hurt me.

LIFE WITHOUT MY MEDS

A day without my meds is
A minute without oxygen,
An hour without colour.
Each pain slices through me.
Beyond intense,
Cramps paralyse,
Adhesions attack.

Most of my day spent
Sitting on the seat,
Turning the toilet roll
Round and round
As shit
Burns my skin
Over and over.

TOUCH

Lips locked,
Hands in hair,
Hips pressed
Together:
His hands
Lift my shirt,
Run across
My chest,
Down my body.
I slap

                               his hand away,

Ignoring the hurt
In his eyes.

CLAWING AT MY SKIN

I won't let him

Hug me,
Kiss me,
Touch me.

I recoil

When his fingers
Search for mine.

I make excuses

When he tries
To hold me close
At night.

He may not feel
My scars
But I feel them always
Swirling through my blood,
Clawing at my mind,
Pulsing under my skin.

TOM

I met Tom
On a night out.
Fist pumping to pop anthems,
Our worlds collided,
Our lips connected and
My world was turned
Upside down.

LOSE YOURSELF

We watched movies,
Ate pizza in bed,
Walked through Dublin,
Fingers grazing.
Sipping coffee,
People watching,
Fascinated me.
Easy to lose yourself
When you feel something
So strongly.

EVERYWHERE

Something is wrong here.
I wake,
Bleary-eyed.
I roll onto my side –
My boxers feel heavier.
Something wet coats
My lower back.
My hands probe the sheets:
It's seeped into the mattress.
Tom is dozing on his side.
I don't know how I can clean this
Without him knowing.
Tom, I whisper.
He doesn't stir.
I try again and he rolls over.
I gesture to the bed and
That snaps him back
Into reality.
It's fine, he tells me,
But it is not fine
Because I know that he is
A nurse.
I do not want to be
Viewed under a microscope –
A patient.

I gather my things,
Climb into the taxi
In soiled boxers and jeans,
Praying the driver doesn't smell,
Praying he doesn't speak to me
Because any words will
BREAK me.

OK

I
Do not call,
Do not text,
Do not see him anymore.
Shame permeates my body:
What could I say
To make any of this
OK?

SWIPE

Swiping left,
Swiping right
On a screen:
Hoping to meet
The one.

Swipe left,
Swipe right:
Twink.
Daddy.
Bear.
Is he loyal?
Faithful?
Trustworthy?

Swipe left,
Swipe right:
Masc 4 masc.
Straight acting,
Discrete.
Does he like theatre?
Movies?
Music?

Swipe left,
Swipe right:

No femmes.
No fats.
No Asians.
Can he handle your scars?
Your broken body?
Your top-bunk role?

Swipe left:
He does not like you.

Swipe left:
Can never love you.

Swipe left:
Will *never* love you.

SWORDS AND BAYONETS

Words sharper than
Swords and bayonets
Slice my skin.

The harshest words
Heard in
My own mind.

This prison
Confines me,
Muddies reality and fantasy.

MAP

My scars map out
The latitudes and longitudes
Of the Bermuda Triangle:
A journey few dare make.
I am a no-go area,
My skin covered
In lines and holes,
Marking me out as
A deadly destination.

RECIPE FOR MY LIFE

Pull the thorns
From an anxiety rose.
Fry lightly,
Adding two drops
Of fear essence.
Chop two bulbs of panic and
Add to the sauce.
Set the pan of self-loathing
To two-hundred degrees.
Wish.
Watch.
Wait.
Daily.

MOMENTS OF CLARITY

In moments of clarity,
I hate myself for letting
Thoughts of my scar
Burrow deep in my mind,
Holding emotions and thoughts hostage.

It's just a scar.
It's not that large.
You're making a big deal
Out of nothing.

Maybe it's not
A big deal to you because
You don't have it.
Try telling that to my mind.

DARKNESS

The darkness is an ally;
A place where scars cannot be seen
As fingers inch down my body.
I can hide it,
Mask it,
Make it part of the dance.
I can manipulate conversation;
Reveal something small
To protect something sacred.

The darkness is an enemy;
A place that houses
Pain and fears,
Nightmares that plague me.
It's a silent storm,
Invading my mind,
When the lights go out.

TRAPPED

The floor is solid beneath my feet.
I am safe
Despite the voice
In my head
Telling me
I'm not good enough,
Will never be good enough,
That I am broken,
Bothersome,
A burden to
The boys I date.
The waves of anxiety,
Disappointment,
Insecurity
Sweep me away,
Banish me to my past
Where I play and replay
Every failed relationship,
Hospital visit,
Embarrassing moment
Of this illness.
The floor is solid beneath my feet.
No guardian angel
To swoop in and
Save me.
I am safe.
I wish I believed this.

SUNNY DISPOSITIONS

In darker times,
I remember grandad,
A gentleman who could make me
See light when there were only
Shadows.
His surgery was the first
Of its kind
Performed in Ireland.
Doctors butchered his body.
I am thankful for his sacrifice,
Saddened he had to endure a pain
Greater than mine,
In his moments of weakness
He threw me up into the clouds
Where dreams were real and
My life was as great
As I imagined it to be.
My grandad was a sick man:
FAP,
Three heart attacks but
It was kidney stones
That claimed his life.
I got to share four years
With the greatest man in my life,
Brightening my most banal days
With his sunny disposition.

NEVER STOP DREAMING

Anything is possible
With a grandad
Who holds you up,
Helping you soar
Through the sky
In compassionate arms.
Climbing over walls
To break the glass ceiling.
Easy to do
With a guardian angel
In your corner.

Choke-hold mortgages,
Relationships and
Big-city life will
Threaten happiness,
Test limits
If you let it.
It's easy to feel alone
But then I think of grandad,
Reminding myself:

Never stop dreaming.

DIFFERENT

Lingering smells,
Explosive sounds,
Ridicule:
Some of the reasons
I will not use the toilet
In houses
Other than my own.
I will cramp,
Double over but
Never use the bathroom
For fear
Of being seen
As different.

SHARING SECRETS

Mam is in a good mood.
She takes our plates into the kitchen.
I follow,
Is now a good time
To tell my secret?
She's smiling and laughing,
Tears in her eyes.
I seize my chance:
Mam,
I have something to tell you.
She turns slowly,
Smiling still,
With raised eyebrows.

I'm gay.

These two words
Undo the mood
In the room.

You're joking?

I shake my head.
Words hang heavy
In the air.
I cannot claw them back.

A tear trickles down her cheek.
She hurls herself through the door.
Bracing palms against
Cool marble counters.
The door slams
On illness,
On her grandparent dreams,
On my lifeline,
Anchoring me
To the here and now.

WHAT HAVE I DONE?

Mam doesn't come out of her room.
Dad asks me what's wrong;
I cannot bring myself
To tell him.

My sister knows;
I told her months ago.
She accepted it,
Accepted me as I am.

I do not understand
Mam's reaction.
Two days locked in a room,
Crying.

Why is she taking this so hard?
It's all I can think about;
At college and work,
My mind is always on her.

What have I done?

I AM A GAY

Mam books an appointment
With the doctor
To discuss my sexuality.

How it is his business?

We enter the room,
Walls move in
On all sides.

What seems to be the matter?

Mam shouts out,
He's gay!

The doctor ponders this,
While mam brings up
My illness.

Our doctor nods his head,
Agreeing with mam's points
Adding a word
Where necessary.

Over his shoulder,
I see him type

In the 'concern' box:
I am a gay.

Our doctor advises us
To see the stoma nurse
To discuss this
Further.

I knew 'coming out' would
Be difficult but
I was not prepared for this.

In my head,
I scream the words:

A

COMPLICATIONS

Mam worries

Being gay
Means complications
She is not sure
I'm ready for.

First-time sex is
A messy, awkward,
Hands-flailing
Act.

I never
Thought about it
But she's
Spot on.

Even
She has no idea
How difficult
This will be.

OFFICIAL SOURCES

Mariam's office
Brings back
Memories:
Emptying and changing
Ileostomy bags,
Preparing for a life
Altered by scalpels and stitches.

This is outside my control,
Making it a hundred times worse than
All the surgeries combined.
I cannot influence mam's thoughts,
Cannot beg and plead
For support.
Sitting beside her:
Embarrassment,
Shame,
Fear,
Spike my senses
Into high alert.

She held my hand
During the surgeries
But, now,
The six inches
Between our chairs

May as well be
Six countries apart.

Wedged between mam and
The office wall,
Mariam confirms my deepest fears:
A relationship with a boy
Will be hard to work,
Sex with another man could
Hurt me,
Make me haemorrhage
Or, worse,
Kill me.
Something I already knew
But am shocked
To hear
From official sources.

DAD

My father
Liked to drink beer,
Played football at the weekends.
He enjoyed sports and TV,
Choosing to spend most of his time
Alone.

After his brain injury,
He is much the same man,
Though lazier.

Mam tells me that
She told my father
I am gay,
My mind races.
I call my friends,
Talking it through.
Terror stops my tears
In their tracks.

A

knock

sounds on my door.

He wants to speak to you,
My mother tells me,
Like it's no big deal.
But it is.
My father —
The man's man —
Knows who I am and
That.
Terrifies.
Me.

I open his bedroom door,
Venturing into the lion's den.
I step to the side of his bed,
Waiting for him to speak . . .

CHOKED UP

Dad tells me
He's there if I want
To talk —
A day,
A week,
A year.
He wants me
To know that
He is there.
It catches me off guard,
Choking me with emotion.

SUPERMAN

My dad knowing I'm gay
May not sound a big deal.
It's a bit like Superman
Revealing he's Clark Kent.
When someone reveals
Their deepest secret,
It's like someone taking
A knife to your heart,
Cutting through
Muscle,
Blood,
Tissue,

Right to the core.

STIGMA

Stigma:
A small word,
Laced with more
Derision than its
Arrangement of sounds suggests.

A SUIT OF ARMOUR

A

suit of

A R M O U R

C   chipped   C

H   away at,   H

I   trembling   I

P   in iron boots   P

waiting for

The next blow to

strike   flesh

sever   arteries

break   bones

THE BINARY GAME

To be hetero is
To be happy —
To like women:
The norm.
If you don't fit the box,
Shape yourself
Around the labels,
You're different.
Queer.
Gay.
They call you names,
Pick at your difference:
Faggot,
Fairy,
Bender —
Words that cut deeper than
Glass that they launch,
Fists that they throw,
Kicks that rain down
On bodies that
Did nothing
To deserve them.
Hetero,
Homo,
Man,
Woman,

Black,
White —
We are all
Human.

FIRST BOYFRIEND

Daniel:
My first boyfriend.
He says that
He loves me,
Just the way I am.
My brain waits
For the punchline.
How can anyone
Love me
With these hideous scars
Marring my body?
I do not believe him.
I *cannot* believe his platitudes.

HEAT

Wrap your arms
Around me,
Fingertips grazing hair,
Setting nerve endings
On fire.

Down.
Down.
Down.

Hands searching
The plains of my body,
Inching slowly
Towards my scar.

I clasp his wrist,
Drop his hand,
Leave his bed.

I run to the toilet,
Bolt the door,
Sink to the floor,
Heat lost
To cold tiles.

DANIEL

Daniel didn't see
What the mirror revealed:
The black hole
Sucking in
My beauty.

It's all in your head —
Easy for him
To say
When he doesn't know
What's inside my mind.

NO IDEA

I eat and drink
With Daniel,
Watch movies and
Hold hands
As we sit on the couch
Eating pizza.
But when the movie is over,
When we share a bed,
I cannot relax
Into him,
Let his hands wander
The plains of my body.
I fear he will
Feel the scar and
See me the way
Everyone else does —

The way I do.

LOVE AND SEX

The difference between
Love and sex is
A promise
Cemented in trust.
I've experienced
Hands-in-hair happiness,
Sweaty sensuality
Dripping down scorching skin and
The magical madness
Of everything you are
Intertwining someone else's
Everything.
I've never trusted anyone
Enough to open the door and
Let my sea of secrets spill out.
Love binds my throat,
Clogs my pores but
It never escapes into
The arms of an awaiting lover.

ANXIETY

I
Lie
Beside him
Body blanketed
Under his gaze
This is a game
Played over and over
Different days
Different seasons
Same old dance
With darkness
I can guide his gaze
But fingers
Feel all

PILLS

Pills control the physical,
Struggle to control emotion,
Will never master thought.
There is no pill
To remind us
To live,
To love,
To be.
No pill
To unshackle
Your mind,
Let you
Be free.

SPECTATOR SPORT

Mental health is
Not a spectator sport –
Not a football game
Like the ones I watched
With dad
When I was eight.
Fans cheered,
Drank beer,
Crunched crisps,
As players kicked balls
Into a net.
Among thousands,
I felt the crowd walls
Cave in,
Puncture air from lungs,
Electrify nerves.
A smile on the outside
While I shrivelled on the inside.

I'M MAD.
REALLY

The woman
On the train

Glares at me

For not giving up my seat.
She doesn't know that
Folded arms
Across my tummy are
The only thing
Keeping the cramps
At bay.

MAD!

I close my eyes,
Breathing deep.
Cocooning myself
From piercing glares.

INVISIBLE ILLNESS

When your arms and legs function,
When your eyes see,
When your mouth moves,
It makes it difficult
For people to know
You are suffering
On the inside.

ABCS

A is for apple
B is for ball
C is for car —
Things we can
Taste,
Touch,
Smell,
See,
Hear.

Tangible objects are
Vibrating atoms.
These things are science:
Learned and understood,
Developed young,
Unlike
Mental health.

There is no A–Z
For mental health that
Helps us grasp something we cannot
Experience with the senses.
We cannot see it,
Sometimes struggle to prove it,
To comprehend it and
Push forward

With much-needed research
To develop
Understanding and awareness
Of our powerful but fragile minds.
A is for anxiety
B is for bipolar disorder
C is for compulsive personality —
Invisible illnesses that we choose
To live in ignorance of
Until it happens to
Us.

FLESH AND BONE

Flesh and bone,
Feeling and fear:
We are all human,
All love,
All see
What we want to.
We think differently.
Difficult to understand but
Easy to judge
Something,
Someone,
You do not know.

OPPORTUNITIES

Admitting a disability
Feels a lot like
Revealing a weakness —
Painting a bull's eye on your chest
So the world can gawk
At your vulnerabilities.
Equal opportunities make me shudder.
Do I disclose my disability?
Reveal limitations or hold them close?
Do I admit my dark secret or
Bury it deep?
Do you have a disability?
No.
Something pricks my stomach
As I press SEND
On another job application.

MY FIRST JOB

My first job:
Packing shelves
With toys.
Children run around the store,
Chased by shouting parents
While upstairs,
Amy and Annalise
Puff cigarettes
On the hour
Every hour.
I cannot empty my bowels
Without a torrent of questions yet
They can smoke
Whenever they see fit —
No questions asked.
I press my right hand
To my stomach,
Staving off cramps
While my left hand
Stocks shelves.

GOOD ENOUGH

At the gym,
I lift weights,
Run on treadmills and
Repeat ab crunches
When the pains attack.

I double over,
Hating the disconnect
Between body and goals.
I want to be fit,
To be handsome,
To be loved.

In the changing room,
I sit,
Breathe deep,
Thinking about
All the ways
I am not good enough.

TRUE BEAUTY

True beauty
Cycles from trend to trend:
One day you're in,
The next you're out.
You can
Slice yourself skinny,
Bleach your skin,
Dye your hair but
You will always be that person.
If you can't love yourself
Then you'll become
A cult follower.

It's easy to feel
You don't belong in this world:
Attractive actors,
Sexy singers,
Six-packs and skinny minis
Decorating the covers
Of glossy magazines.
Easy to fall
Into a depression
From which escape
Feels impossible.
Bombarded with
En-vogue pretty that

Starts and finishes
With size zero.
It's easy to believe
You are the problem
When you are the symptom
Of a society
Callous and skin deep.

BODY IMAGE

TV,
Movies,
Magazines —
I try to escape
Body image.
It's everywhere:
#instafit
#fitstagram
#fitfamily.
Un-social media
Tells us to be fit is
To be happy.
Happiness comes from the inside;
It does not come from
Bar bells and treadmills,
Green diets and protein shakes.
It comes from the people
Who love us,
The people that
Laugh with us and
The people that
Teach us.
I look at oiled-up models
Telling myself that I'm not them.
My body is scarred,
Flawed,

But it is mine.
I cannot control my body,
Control how others see me,
But I can look in the mirror,
Learn to love my reflection.

RAW EMOTION

People see my blue eyes
Brown hair,
Clear skin,
Assuming
I am healthy
Because the shell is
Shining.

On the inside,
A storm rages,
Struggling to find ground
Amid a tsunami
Of raw emotion.

FRESH BEGINNING

I hold the letter
Between dry hands,
Running my fingers
Over sharp corners.
I remember letters
Announcing
Blood tests,
Colonoscopies,
Surgeries,
But this is different.
This is a fresh beginning
To slice away the shadows
That feed on my every thought.

ST VINCENT'S HOSPITAL

All glass and white brick,
St Vincent's Hospital is
Magnificent,
Mam and I
Walk up to reception,
Filling out forms,
Following directions.
The interior is cavernous,
Palm trees thrive
Under a transparent roof.
We step into the elevator,
Ascending to the third floor
Where Dr Lawlor's waiting room
Awaits.

LIBERATION

I should be anxious
But I'm relieved that
This journey is
Coming to an end.
I have spent years
Gazing into the mirror
At a monster,
Concealing my body
From lovers,
Friends,
Myself.
Can I finally live
Without loathing?

DR LAWLOR

Dr Lawlor
Reads my file,
Examines the scar,
Types her notes
As she explains that
My scar is a fascia:
Caused when scar tissue
Heals over the skin.
An easy same-day procedure,
She tells me,
Outlining what will happen,
When it will happen and
How it will heal.
I leave the office
Glowing and confident.

WRISTBAND

Sodium lamps
Burn orange
In semi-darkness
As I make my way
To the hospital,
Tucked into my long coat
In the early-morning chill.
I take a number,
Wait my turn
To register
For a wristband.

UNDERSTANDING

I put on the gown,
Understanding that today means
No more abyss,
No more hole in my belly.
I wave goodbye to mam
As the porter wheels me
To theatre.
I stare into
The black-hole scar
For the last time.

SOON-TO-BE LIFE

Dr Lawlor checks in
As the anaesthetist
Fits the mask over
Nose and mouth.
My last thoughts
My last thoughts
Float into the air.
Gas fills my lungs,
Making my lids heavy,
Dissipating thoughts
Of my soon-to-be life.

TIME TO HEAL

The scar
Tender,
Red raw
And sore.
The surgeon
Says it
Will heal.
I'm sure
She's right,
She knows
What she's
Talking about
But there's
A part
Of me
That's scared
That this
Mark will
Stain my
Skin forever.
A constant
Reminder of
The pain,
The fear,
The trauma
Of this

Illness I
Never
Asked for.
Everywhere
I'm reminded of
Limitations,
Weaknesses,
Vulnerabilities
That make
Me less
Than human.

LOSING MYSELF

Even though the surgery was
Fairly straightforward —
Cutting out the fascia and
Sewing the skin together —
It requires bed rest and
Breathing exercises.
I try not to cough,
Not to laugh too hard
Because the pain
Cuts like a knife —
Similar to adhesions.
I can't
Run,
Exercise,
Swim.
Instead,
I'm working my way
Through a pile of books.
Losing myself
In someone else's world is
Less painful than
Living in my own.

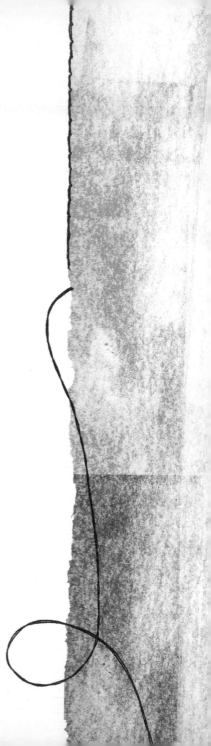

FOLLOW-UP

Dr Lawlor
Peels back the bandage.
I hold my breath,
Unsure what to expect.
The scar is still there,
A bit purple.
Doctor Lawlor tells me
This is normal,
As she removes the stitches.
It takes several weeks
To fully heal.
If it doesn't,
I can have more surgery.
No,
I tell her.
I don't need more surgery.
My illness is inextricably me.
I'm free to be me
Despite what others say.
I've owned my pain and
I'll own this new scar
As a reminder
Of everything I am,
Everything I can be.

GREATEST ASSET

My personality is
My greatest asset,
My greatest weapon
But when it comes to dating,
I am too feminine
Not masculine,
Not muscular enough.

My body is scarred
From belly button
To below my hips.
My sense of self cannot grow
Amongst ivy that
Chokes life from all else.

I do not know
What species I am,
Only that I will not
Be smothered
By labels and limits.
My personality is
My greatest asset.

ACCEPTANCE

There comes a point
In your life
When you stop reading
About green diets and
Regimented routines
Of water and honey
To achieve the body beautiful,
When you stop opening your mouth
To consume impossible standards and
Delude yourself into thinking that
Skinny + money = happiness.
You start questioning the source,
Demanding the credentials
Of the person telling you
To lose weight
You don't need to lose.

Who is telling me
I'm not good enough?

For a long time,
I was obsessed with my body,
Trying to be leaner
To compensate for a scar
I couldn't accept.
But it wasn't the physical scar

That needed to heal.
I needed to accept myself
As I am.
What anyone else thinks is
None of my business.

FATHER

My father
And I:
We will
Never see
Eye to eye.
Love-crumpled notes:
His way of showing
Love.
I must accept him
As he is.

I can resist
All I want,
Fight
For the father
I needed
But none of this will
Change anything,
Alter the past,
Mould the present.
I cannot change him
But I can chart
My own future.

I AM NOT BRAVE

I am not brave:
Not someone
Who has saved lives,
Fought to lead,
Changed the world.

As a boy,
I had an illness:
Something I am
Still accepting
Today.

Years on:
I have days
Both good and bad,
Times that confine
Me to my mind,
Others,
When I am free.

I still work
Through the scars
On body,
In mind,
Telling myself:
I am good enough.

I will not let
These feelings win out
When I have
Overcome so much.

The surgeries did not
Defeat me,
Did not break me
In my darkest moment.
They kept me down
But I got back up,
Stepped into the ring
To confront
The voice in my head.

A mind-altering anxiety,
A deafening depression
That boxed me in,
Stopped me
Being me.

I will not be loved
By all,
I will be a brother to one,
A friend to some,

An example
For many:
The only thing
Keeping you down
Is
You.

BREATHE

It comes as
A shot in the dark,
A shock to the system
When the cramps attack.
Echoes from the past.
Doubled over,
Hands pressed to belly,
They claim me.
Five years on,
But,
I have learned to

Breathe,

Think fluidly,

Live more freely –

Unburdened by

The pains of my past.

Regular check-ups

Unearth past nightmares of

Fear,

Despair,

Opposition.

I wear my own skin,
Proud of my body —
Scars and all.
Free from
The psychological prison,
I can be

Felt,
Touched,
Loved,

Without self-loathing.
Lying with lovers;
An act of celebration —
Who,
What,
Why
We are.
Welcoming warmth
Into my life
Where shadows and monsters

Once ruled my mind.
The white torpedoes
Monitor my illness,
Control pain and
Slow down bowel movements,
But I am
More than
Medication,
Illness,
Anxieties.
Ten years of fighting:
Every day a battle
But I must remember
Not to forget
To live
Because, now,

I

Can

Breathe.

WHICH CHRIS WILL THEY SEE?

Meeting new people
For the first time is
A conundrum.
Which Chris will they see?
How much should I let them know?
Will I tell them about my illness?
Talking makes it easier
To accept myself and
For others that will
Come after me,
Others that will face
The same ignorance,
The same adversity,
The same thoughts.
If someone asks about my illness,
I always tell them:
Even if they don't understand,
Might never understand.
I try to make a difference.

PAPERCUT

Words flow from the pen
Like blood from a wound,
Blotting out fears,
Building me up
Higher than ever.
I don't know how
To be vulnerable.
I'll keep writing,
Keep learning
Until I am
Free to embrace
Who I am.

I AM...

Son,
Brother,
Nephew
Refusing
To be defined
By physical scars
Criss-crossing my body.
Conquering
Crippling cramps,
Aggressive adhesions,
Late-night leakages –
Threatening time
Spent with loved ones.

I am
The boy,
The teenager,
The man
Who overcame
Adversity,
Accepted who I am,
Embraced my difference,
Banishing dark thoughts
From my mind.
Victorious over
Bullies,

Anxiety,
Surgery –
Holding
Sense of self
Hostage.

I am
A lover,
A partner,
A boyfriend –
Refusing to be limited
By illness.
Overcoming
Diagnosis,
Treatment,
Aftermath –
Complications
Rippling into
My relationships,
My mind,
My perspective,
Closing me off
From being hurt
By strangers
Who do not
Understand.

I know
Who I am,
What I am,
Why I am ...

I am Christopher George Moore.

ACKNOWLEDGEMENTS

I owe more than I'll ever be able to pay to my mam.
She stood by me every step of the way; through every
appointment, every surgery, every tear. Though we have
our ups and downs, she has and will always be the warrior
fighting my corner. I am so grateful to my grandad who
taught me the power of compassion and resilience from
such a young age. Thank you to my dad and Georgina
(you act like you have a heart of ice, but I know better!).

As always, this book would not be what it is today without
the keen editorial eye and dedication from my editor and
best friend, Jake. You inspire me every day to continue
writing.

Anna, Marie and Jackie: thank you for supporting me
and raving about my books.

To Ann: thank you for being one of the first booksellers
to stock *Fall Out* and for championing my books.

Thank you to Tanja, Alison, Amy and all the people at
Youth Libraries Group that have supported me.

A special thank you to Lena, Teasie, Gary and Anna
who were there for me during the most difficult years
of my life. Your kindness and love are never forgotten.

To everyone at UCLan Publishing and Bounce: this wouldn't be possible without you. Hazel: thank you immensely for taking a chance on *Gut Feelings* and for all the amazing support and promotion you've given my books. A massive thank you to Becky for taking my words and transforming them into something magical and mesmerising. Not to mention the spectacular cover!

Danielle: thank you for the advice and moral support on my writing journey.

My thanks too to all the authors who have given quotes and the bloggers who read and review my books, and to the booksellers who stock them. *Gut Feelings* is a story that is close to my heart and I hope you enjoy reading it as much as I loved writing it. I hope this book helps bring more compassion and understanding for those living with disability and invisible illness.

ADDITIONAL INFORMATION ABOUT FAP

I was 11 years old when I was diagnosed with Familial Adenomatous Polyposis (or FAP). FAP is a rare genetic illness that is caused by a defect in the adenomatous polyposis coli gene (or APC gene). Although I, and the majority of those diagnosed, inherited the gene from a parent, for about 25–30% of people, the genetic mutation occurs spontaneously. As it's a rare illness, there are no specific statistics for the number of people that have FAP, but estimates vary from 1 in 22,000 up to 1 in 7,000.

The presence of colorectal polyps can indicate the need for biopsies and their removal. This will give surgeons a better indication for diagnosis.

The procedure is performed with a small, long, flexible tube known as a colonoscope which is inserted into the rectum. A tiny video camera at the tip of the tube allows the doctor to view the inside of the entire colon.

At 12, I had my first colonoscopy. Where they expected to see polyps in double digits, they saw thousands and they were growing more rapidly than they had thought. As a result, I had a total colectomy, resulting in the removal of my entire colon. This bought me time for my next surgery at 17 where surgeons cut out the lining of the rectum and created an ileal-anal pouch (or a J-pouch). I had a stoma which emptied into an ileostomy bag for five months to allow this to heal and in December 2008, I had the reversal. I no longer have an ileostomy bag, but I do have a J-pouch.

There are a number of resources and supports available if you are diagnosed with FAP or any colorectal illness.

For readers in Ireland: If you or someone close to you is worried about or affected by cancer, you can get free information, support and advice from the Irish Cancer Society.

Call their Freephone Support Line on **1800 200 700** or visit **www.cancer.ie**

For readers in the UK: Macmillan Cancer Support is there to help everyone with cancer live life as fully as they can, providing physical, financial and emotional support. So whatever cancer throws your way, they're right there with you.

For information, support or just someone to talk to, call **0808 808 00 00** (7 days a week, 8am–8pm) or visit **macmillan.org.uk**

To give, fundraise or volunteer, call **0300 1000 200** or visit **macmillan.org.uk**

HAVE YOU EVER WONDERED HOW BOOKS ARE MADE?

UCLan Publishing are based in the North of England
and involve BA Publishing and MA Publishing students
from the University of Central Lancashire at every
stage of the publishing process.

BA Publishing and MA Publishing students work closely
alongside the company and work on producing books as part
of their course – some of which are selected to be published
and printed by UCLan Publishing. Students also gain first-hand
experience conceiving and running innovative high-level
events to leverage sales, as well as running content
creation business enterprises.

Our approach to business and teaching has been recognized
academically and within the publishing industry. We have been
awarded Best Newcomer at the Independent Publishing Guild
Awards (2019) and a *Times* Higher Education Award
for Excellence and Innovation in the Arts (2018).

As our business continues to grow, so too does the experience
our students have upon entering UCLan Publishing.

To find out more, please visit
www.uclanpublishing.com/courses/